Y0-BXV-867

Beneath Land and Sea

by the author of

BENEATH
LAND AND SEA

by Aylesa Forsee

with illustrations by James Heugh

MACRAE SMITH COMPANY: PHILADELPHIA

Foreword

More is known about the stars millions of miles away than about the earth only a few miles beneath our feet; yet there are challenges beneath the land and sea more significant than that of putting a man on the moon.

One of the biggest questions facing the world today is, How shall we supply enough food, fuel, water, and power for exploding populations when shortages exist already? Submarine and subterranean scientists are investigating the possibilities of obtaining food from the sea, petroleum from beneath it, water from hidden underground wells and power from the subsurface plumbing of geysers. These same scientists are also trying to find out how man can protect himself from the violence of the underground forces of earthquakes and volcanoes.

Archaeologists excavating in lost cities, paleontologists chipping out coal balls in mines, seismologists studying the behavior of waves relayed to Earth's warm heart—all are attempting to explain the peculiarities of man's planet. Submarine and subterranean scientists are working on questions put to them by industry, the Navy and the government. Will dumping atomic waste in the ocean contaminate the creatures in it? What caves are suitable for military storage depots, shelters, command posts, and communication centers? What effect does temperature of the water have on sonar devices used in submarine detection?

This book describes some of the methodology of oceanographers, geologists, geophysicists, paleontologists and archaeologists who concentrate on subsurface phenomena, but it does not pretend to be a complete survey of these branches of science. Its primary concern is with the questions and challenges confronting scientists who deal with fossils and forces, artifacts and resources now locked beneath land and sea. The answers are vital not only to science but to our survival.

AYLESA FORSEE

Contents

1

Science of the Sea

How many fish are in the ocean? Will dumping atomic waste in the water contaminate them? Is it true that there is enough gold in the sea to make every individual in the world wealthy? Will depth ships permit exploration of underwater canyons and mountains? Would atomic bombing of Arctic ice caps provide a new highway for commerce, or would it produce another Ice Age? Can men farm the sea? What new resources lie hidden there?

Oceanographers' answers to such questions promise more, in terms of human welfare, than the answers brought back by rockets, satellites and spacemen. The interplanetary space race is exciting and dramatic, but so is the depth exploration of the earth, and the water that covers two-thirds of its surface.

Dr. Roger R. Revelle, who is Director of the Scripps Institution of Oceanography when not acting as scientific adviser to the Department of Interior, facetiously describes an oceanographer as "a sailor who uses a lot of big words." Actually the term is applied to geologists, chemists, geophysicists, or biologists working on projects having to do with the sea.

Oceanographers carry on much research in land-based laboratories, but they also work in floating ones. Most of the laboratory ships are small vessels that were originally built to serve as mine sweepers, fishing craft or yachts. Columbia University's Lamont Geological Observatory, a center for research in oceanography and earth sciences, converted a thirty-seven year old auxiliary schooner,

Vema, into a research ship. A machine shop replaced the paneled main dining room. The afterdeck salon became a laboratory shack. Two hundred feet long, the *Vema* could carry a crew of eighteen plus a dozen scientists and technicians.

Oceanographic vessels put to sea to find answers to specific questions. The purpose may be a census of marine life in a certain area, ocean depth studies, exploration of a submarine canyon, or removal of cores from beneath the ocean floor to provide ages-old sediments for geophysical study. Such expeditions are usually financed by the Navy, a science foundation or an oceanographic institution such as Woods Hole or Scripps Institution of Oceanography of the University of California.

Laboratory ships cost well over a thousand dollars a day to operate, and oceanographers feel obligated to make every minute of their time count. The staff of scientists may start work at four in the morning and then spend all day and much of the night extracting information from the dark reaches below.

Routines include doing seismic tests for depth, measuring currents by meters, snapping pictures of sea creatures or recording readings from an array of instruments. To find out how cold, how salty or how populated an undersea area is, oceanographers use cables, cameras, thermometers and plankton traps. Sonar devices provide a sort of sixth sense for underwater exploration.

Oceanographers aboard research vessels are constantly checking the temperature of the water. A continuous recording to the depth of several hundred feet may be obtained by towing a thermistor chain. There are also electrical recording devices which when lowered to the ocean floor record both temperature and depth.

Taking a hydro-station is an important chore in the oceanographer's day. This requires putting down a string of recording thermometers and water sampling bottles. On some vessels, in order to attach the instruments to the winch cable, the scientist has to climb out on a swinging, pivoted plank, or "hero board," projecting over the water. When the sea is calm and weather warm, this is no great task, but in rough weather it is both uncomfortable and dangerous.

OCEANOGRAPHERS AT WORK

Information gained from hydro-station statistics is valuable to weather forecasters, because ocean temperatures have a bearing on the path of hurricanes as well as on fog, sun or shadows affecting inland areas.

During the season when icebergs are most likely to cast off fragments, the coldness of the water in the vicinity gives navigators warnings of submerged ice. Because of the sensitivity of submarine detection instruments to changes in temperatures, naval officials consult oceanographic charts. Since temperature affects life in the sea, marine biologists are also interested in hydro-station records. Appreciable warming of the water can trigger a massive migration of fish.

Creatures of the sea also react to density of the water, which is altered by temperature, salinity and pressure. To measure the density, oceanographers use sampling bottles that gulp water for analysis. These vary in type, but most of them have trick covers that open and shut at designated depths. High salt content and low temperatures make the water heavier and denser.

Oceanographers compile the evidence accumulated by bottles, traps, thermometers, and sonar devices; then classify and analyze findings, and discuss problems with their colleagues. At intervals during their round-the-clock schedules they snatch a few bites of food. During brief periods of sleep they dream of ingenious gadgets that could be anchored in position to record temperatures and density of the water for a year at a time.

Life on oceanographic vessels is never easy. Equipment operates noisily. Living space is limited. Furniture has to give way to apparatus. The laboratory is crowded and likely to be poorly ventilated.

When the coring apparatus balks or the wire snarls on a piston corer, oceanographers are forced into becoming fix-it-yourself operators and emerge with nicked hands. Research ships, because they are small, often have a quick, easily triggered rolling motion, making seasickness a problem. Storms sometimes menace the lives of those on board.

On January 13, 1954, the *Vema,* two hundred miles north of Bermuda, was battling high winds and a mountainous sea. Dr. Maurice

Ewing, director of the Lamont Geological Observatory, his younger brother John, and the first and second mates volunteered to lash down oil drums that had broken loose on the deck, but a huge wave rolling across the deck swept all four of the men overboard. First mate Charles Wilkie drowned. The other three men freed themselves from hampering clothing and clung to floating oil drums. After three-quarters of an hour, the *Vema* crew succeeded in rescuing them. Rough-hewn "Doc" had received injuries that partly paralyzed him for a month and left him with a slight but permanent limp.

Such crises are infrequent, and oceanographers seem to be a rugged lot, well fitted to cope with discomfort and danger. Most of them, genuinely in love with science and the sea, meet challenges zestfully. Dr. Ewing, even after his narrow escape, still went to sea on an average of three months out of every year.

The study of oceans is just emerging from the stage of exploration to the exactitude of a full-fledged science. Already oceanographers are helping to make long-range weather forecasting possible. Through their mapping and exploration of currents, icebergs and submarine canyons, they have contributed much to the speed and safety of ships at sea.

One of the most encouraging developments is the ten-year program set up by the Office of Naval Research. The Navy's interest in oceanography began during World War II, when oceanographers, through their knowledge of the behavior of sound underwater, solved problems related to submarines. Since then, development of atomic submarines and guided missiles has made the oceans of the world strategic defense areas.

Only oceanographers have a thorough knowledge of the conditions that would govern underwater warfare. To improve the quantity and quality of their information, the Navy has set up a program making funds available to add to the staffs and shore facilities of sea research institutions.

Gaps in oceanographic knowledge are being filled in by a survey of the North Atlantic and Arctic oceans undertaken by the American Geographical Society, with an advisory panel of the National

Academy of Sciences' National Research Council. Regional maps have been distributed to scientists in many fields—geographers, geologists, biologists and physicists, to mention a few. Each will fill in a map for a designated area giving whatever information he can about fish, plant life, temperature, currents, depths, or sediments. After the research has been completed, maps will be returned to the Geographical Society, which will evaluate, correlate, and publish them in atlas form, giving a detailed picture of the two oceans from top to bottom, and the creatures inhabiting them. The atlas should be of value not only to scientists but to commercial fisheries and agencies involved in ocean transportation.

Surveys of this type are needed for all the oceans. They can tell scientists whether the supply of salmon, seaweed, copper and cobalt can relieve the alarming depletion of land resources.

However, oceanographers cannot answer these and other questions deluging them without enlarged capabilities for research— ships with greater range and stability, better equipment and more laboratory space. Scientists would like to see more universities with oceanographic departments, and more students enrolling in them.

But even with an upsurge in the number of ships and scientists the burden of research of all the oceans is too heavy for any one nation to carry alone. The solution lies in international cooperation. During the International Geophysical Year beginning July 1, 1957 and ending in December, 1958, many nations pooled their resources in a great, concerted search for the secrets of earth, sea and sky. Scientific teams demonstrated their ability to carry out shared world-wide projects.

Oceanographers showed their interest in that kind of teamwork when they came from all over the world to the first oceans-for-peace conference held at United Nations headquarters in New York. The conference was sponsored by the American Association for the Advancement of Science; the United Nations Educational, Scientific and Cultural Organization; and the Special Committee on Oceanographic Research, which grew out of the International Geophysical

Year. In its way this conference was as significant as an atoms-for-peace conference.

The consensus of the conference was that the time has come for large-scale oceanic experimentation, but such experiments should be undertaken as the result of joint international agreement. Tinkering with the ocean without sufficient knowledge could be extremely dangerous. Some oceanographers are aghast at a project, much discussed by the Russians, for using atomic bombs to blast through the Arctic ice cap.

Such a project might clear a new shipping lane, but oceanographers point out that icy winds would absorb moisture from the water thus exposed. At the prevailing Arctic temperature, snow would be inevitable. Dumped onto nearby lands, the snow could pack into glaciers that would start creeping southward, thus initiating a new Ice Age.

2

Currents, Echoes and Waves

Woods Hole oceanographers, curious about the forces that produce currents and waves, built a tank that reproduced in miniature the oceans of the western hemisphere. Rubber models of continents supplied the land masses. Air blown from nozzles mounted on the circular rim simulated wind, and heat lamps took the place of the sun. To give the effect of the earth's rotation, the tank revolved at speed up to ten revolutions per minute. By dropping blobs of colored ink into the water, scientists reproduced the circulation patterns for the entire hemisphere.

Such experiments help oceanographers to answer for their own satisfaction questions about the speed and behavior of currents. From data thus accumulated, they can also cope with queries put to them by fishermen, navigators, meteorologists and military strategists. One of these has required a great deal of research. Will dumping atomic waste in the ocean contaminate creatures living in it?

At first the deep, shielded waters seemed to provide the space and remoteness needed. Supporters of the plan maintained that even when containers deteriorated, the waste inside them would not circulate. Correctness of this argument hinged on whether currents are surface manifestations, or whether the sea is in motion at all levels.

During the International Geophysical Year, oceanographers studied the movements of water intensively. The Woods Hole

Atlantis and the British vessel *Discovery II* went looking for the current that oceanographer Henry Stommel of Woods Hole predicted would be flowing under the Gulf Stream and counter to it.

At different depths and places, researchers dumped buoys invented by oceanographer John C. Swallow. This type of buoy, made of strong aluminum tubing, sinks slowly until it reaches a level where the sea water, compressed by the weight of the water above it, has the same density as the buoy. Then it hangs and drifts with the deep water, meanwhile broadcasting strong ultrasonic beeps.

From the pings picked up by sonar devices on the *Atlantis,* oceanographers learned that Stommel's hunch had been correct. Buoys set to float at only a few thousand feet down drifted with the Gulf Stream; those set deeper traveled in the opposite direction.

One of the most interesting discoveries of a current in the depths occurred when the United States Fish and Wildlife Service sent a ship west of the Galapagos Islands to experiment with a Japanese technique of fishing for deep-swimming tuna. While watching the fishermen at work, the late Townsend Cromwell was surprised to see the fish lines drifting eastward while the ship was being carried westward on the well-known South Equatorial Current. He suspected the presence of a powerful current running in the opposite direction.

In 1958, oceanographers from the Scripps Institution of Oceanography confirmed the hidden river's presence by taking scores of subsurface readings. They named it the Cromwell Current. Two hundred and fifty miles wide and three hundred feet below the surface of the ocean, it flows eastward, carrying a thousand times as much water as the Mississippi River.

For additional evidence of subsurface currents, oceanographers have obtained photographs taken in numerous places on the floor of the sea which show ripple marks similar to those caused by tidal movements on sandy beaches. Where there are currents, atomic wastes could circulate.

Oceanographer Columbus Iselin has warned that "lousing up the ocean with atomic waste could louse it up for a thousand years."

He believes atomic materials could eventually contaminate fish as well as the persons who eat them. Not all scientists agree with this viewpoint.

Through their observations of currents, oceanographers have been able to explain much about climate and weather. Peru, although close to the equator, remains cool and foggy most of the year because of the cold Humboldt Current sweeping up from the Antarctic. But every ten years or so a current of warm water —called *El Niño* because it appears near Christmas, the birthday of *El Niño,* the Christ Child—creeps down the coast. The tropical rains that accompany it cause floods and widespread disaster.

Elsewhere in the world, oceanographers and meteorologists working together have proved that a shift in the direction of an ocean current can affect weather for miles inland. Recently, scientists have been asking whether by triggering subtle changes in the circulation of water it would be possible to bring about desired improvements in climate. Many oceanographers believe that if a major current could be shifted slightly, moisture could be brought to an arid coastal area, or reduction of rainfall to a humid one.

Navigators and shippers rely heavily on information about currents supplied to them by oceanographers. Even in these days of Diesel power, ships show a wholesome respect for those arteries of the ocean that carry warm and cold water around the earth. Fighting against them wastes both time and fuel.

Simple observation of Nature provides oceanographers with some clues about currents. Remnants of a long-podded West Indian shrub, arriving on the shores of France, alerted them to a northeasterly current in the Atlantic. When glass floats of a type used by Japanese fishermen showed up on the West Coast of the United States scientists had evidence of the west-east current in the Pacific. In the Arctic, icebergs too large to be affected by wind gave reliable indications of currents by the direction of their drift.

To get information on the speed and direction of currents, oceanographers sometimes launch bottles ballasted so that they float with the neck just awash, or, equipped with a drag, ride just below the surface. Each bottle contains a "Break this bottle" slip and a

21

postcard in a plastic envelope asking the finder to report where he found the bottle and on what date. These cards are printed in several languages. Usually a small reward is offered for the information.

Drift bottles, although cheap, are not always reliable. Oceanographers cannot be sure whether wind or current propelled them. Nor do they know, when a bottle is found on land, how long it may have lain in a given spot. Meters that measure both the direction and velocity of currents are more satisfactory. With the help of meters, buoys and ballasted bottles, oceanographers have compiled a great deal of information on the course and characteristics of currents that is very helpful to navigators.

One of the surprise discoveries has been that surface currents fluctuate fitfully because of changes in the density of the water, or because of land masses and gravity. In the Atlantic where currents meet the formidable land mass of the Americas, waters pile up so that the sea surface slopes to the West about three inches in a thousand miles. The spinning of the earth exerts a deflecting force which turns currents to the right in the Northern hemisphere and to the left in the Southern.

A survey of one of the best-known currents, the Gulf Stream, revised the popular idea of a wide, steady stream majestically carrying heat northward. It is, instead, a system of overlapping currents that whip from side to side and sometimes curl into eddies. They may run fast or slowly, forward or backward.

Oceanographers feel that they are only at the beginning of understanding the great current systems. What actually produces them and how are still mysteries.

Waves are also baffling, but even so, oceanographers are finding more and more answers for navigators seeking safe anchorage and hoping to avoid head winds and storms at sea. Off San Clemente Island, sixty miles from La Jolla, California, twin pressure gauges a thousand feet apart on the ocean floor record pressure changes caused by waves. The higher the waves, the greater the pressure. Information from the gauges is transmitted automatically to Scripps Institution of Oceanography. By a complicated method involving electric computers, the height, length and direction of waves and the probable course of a storm can be ascertained, enabling vessels to navigate the high seas in relatively calm waters, and guiding fishermen and owners of small boats to safe anchorage. Oceanographers are devising new instruments that will increase the accuracy of their predictions.

During World War II, military authorities frequently appealed to oceanographers for statistics on the mechanics of wave motion. The height and origins of breakers and rip tides were of vital significance to those directing shore installations or the operations of naval vessels and landing craft. Before the landings on Sicily, Normandy, and elsewhere, officials made careful studies of predicted surf conditions.

Military officials, shippers, and navigators frequently want information on depth of water as well as on the activity of waves and currents. Tired of struggling with weighted ropes or piano wires, oceanographers began experimenting with echo sounding. They discovered that exploding dynamite in the water created sound waves that traveled downward and bounced back when they hit the floor of the sea. By measuring the travel time of the sound to and from the bottom and using appropriate value for the speed of sound in water, about 4,900 feet per second, oceanographers could estimate the depth at a given point.

But what baffled them was the way the sound waves at times seemed to bend or twist. Further research indicated that the amount of the salt in the water affected the behavior of the sound waves. So did temperature. Also, the strength of the echo response varied with the nature of the material at the bottom of the ocean.

Naval officials, cognizant of the research on sound waves, turned to oceanographers for advice when a Navy destroyer based at Guatánamo, Cuba, shortly before the outbreak of World War II had trouble with its sonar equipment, and a team of scientists came down from Woods Hole Oceanographic Institution. To the leader, tall, smiling Columbus Iselin, officials explained that during mock war maneuvers the destroyer was seeing nonexistent targets and missing real ones. Dunking thermometers in the water, the oceanographic team soon diagnosed the difficulty. The tropical sun had heated the water to a temperature high enough to bend the sound waves. Nothing was wrong with their equipment, the oceanographers assured the Navy.

Impressed by this display of scientific know-how, the Navy again appealed to oceanographers after World War II had erupted—this time in connection with submarines. When taking depth measurements, sonar operators sometimes had trouble because a kind of layer or false bottom obscured the real one. At critical moments when reports indicated enemy submarines in water nearby, the pings given off by sonar detection instruments scattered ineffectually. A German or Japanese submarine might suddenly appear with no warning.

Everything seemed to point to the existence of definite layers that scattered sound waves and permitted enemy submarines to hide in them, or even to move about in them unheard and unseen. What caused these scattering layers? naval officials wanted to know. And how could instruments penetrate them?

Oceanographers launched on an extensive program of underwater listening, using submerged microphones, hydrophones, and an ordinary receiver similar in principle to that used in a dictaphone.

They soon encountered mysterious layers that rose and fell at unpredictable intervals and scattered sound waves. At night a layer might rise as fast as fifteen feet per second. At dawn it sank. Oceanographers studying graphs on sonar equipment noted that the vertical migrations ranged from fifteen hundred to within a hundred feet of the surface. Some extended for miles in area.

Speculation on their composition ranged from microbubbles of air to dense strata of shrimp. Oceanographers finally decided that the layers were composed of a concentration of millions of tiny organisms that rose and fell in response to temperature changes, bending, or refracting, the vibrations sent out by sonar equipment.

As a result of such studies, Dr. Maurice Ewing developed the bathythermograph, an instrument for locating the warm masses of deflecting matter, or "temperature hills," in the sea which permitted enemy submarines to hide in or underneath their sonar-scattering layers. Oceanographers at Woods Hole and at Scripps Institution of Oceanography taught submarine personnel how to use bathythermographs and other instruments to trail their quarry through the jungles of the sea, and how to use scattering layers to their own advantage. By adjusting its buoyancy, a submarine could hide in them or balance between them without being detected by enemy sonar equipment.

Ultrasonic sound transmitters and receivers, means of amplifying return signals, and calibrated scales made detection far more sensitive; but the use of low-frequency sound, whether for depth measurements or submarine detection, does have disadvantages. It is difficult to separate signals from nearby noises such as ship's engines, and to screen the receiver from the transmitter.

Seeking to overcome these problems, Columbus Iselin built a monstrous underwater generator dubbed the Imp, which can be suspended under a ship or built into its hull. This gadget for echo sounding releases a powerful pulse of energy through the water which can be heard above interferences.

Developing a sound-ranging system that can keep all the oceans under surveillance has become a combined project of oceanographers and naval personnel. Part of the research in a project under the code name of Artemis is directed toward developing a system of sound beams that will guide submarine traffic as radar guides aircraft. The ultimate goal is a world-wide network that would tell the speed and location of any submarine in the world.

Instruments and techniques are improving, but scientific exploration of the oceans has been far from adequate. If oceanographers are ever to understand the sea and predict with complete accuracy the behavior of waves, currents, and sonar pings, they need maps, charts and reports from far and wide similar to those supplied meteorologists for making weather forecasts. Instead of information on humidity or cloud formations, the oceanographers require statistics on depth, currents, water temperature and salinity.

In 1959 the National Academy of Science's Committee on Oceanography declared, "Man's knowledge of the oceans is meager indeed compared with their importance to him." That knowledge increases as scientists delve into problems of echo sounding, safe disposal of atomic waste, and the effects of oceans on weather and navigation. Oceanographers are determined to find answers, whether in land-based laboratories or aboard ships sailing the secretive sea.

3

Dwellers in the Depths

Marine biologists are particularly interested in learning about the habits and characteristics of sea creatures that menace man. They hope to find out once and for all how dangerous and annoying are sharks, spiked mantas, fire coral and sea anemones. They want, among other things, to measure the effects of pressure, salinity, absence of light and enormous pressures on the sight, mechanism, activity, and life span of crabs, crayfish, corals and cod, and find out whether there really are serpents in the sea.

Modern scientists have scoffed at the existence of sea serpents, but findings of the Danish oceanographer Dr. Anton Bruin have renewed old rumors. One giant eel larva that he located off the coast of Panama had four hundred and fifty vertebrae, compared with the usual one hundred and fourteen for the common eel. On the premise that each of the vertebrae would measure between one and two inches when fully grown, Dr. Bruin estimated that a mature eel of that species would be a monster more than thirty feet long.

Looking for his answers, a marine biologist spends much time in a laboratory evaluating specimens provided for him. He may, when at sea, strap on an aqualung and descend into tropical waters where he is surrounded by yellow butterfly fish or blue parrot fish swallowing bites of hard coral; but more often he will work from the pitching deck of an oceanographic vessel, using nets, dredges, plankton recorders or waterproof cameras.

Marine biologists use many of the techniques devised by early oceanographers. Nets, on the principle of the tea strainer, are still standard equipment.

One net, invented by a group of biologists headed by John D. Isaacs of the Scripps Institution of Oceanography, has floats that make it buoyant. When it reaches a predetermined depth, the ballast placed in the center detaches itself and then the net opens and rises to the surface like an inverted parachute, scooping up unwary fishes on the way.

Net hauls vary with the region. In some areas a quart of water may prove nearly lifeless, whereas in the Antarctic the water is so crowded with tiny plants and animals that it resembles a murky soup. Sea pastures also vary from season to season. A net dragged through the North Sea in February yielded only four hundred specimens of a certain copepod; two months later the same place yielded four million.

To catch animals living near the ocean bottom, biologists use very large bag nets known as trawls. These may have many special devices, such as tickle chains attached to the foot rope, which disturb the fish and cause them to pass backwards into the trawl as it is dragged through the water. Dredges are also useful for scooping up fish.

Oceanographers aboard ships are always excited by dredge hauls. When the *Galathea*, a Danish oceanographic vessel under the direction of Dr. Bruin, was over the Philippine Trench, everyone on board who could leave his job clustered around the trawl bag when it was hoisted on deck. Biologists, agog over the possibility that some strange new creature had been brought up, paid little attention to red prawn or black fishes. They expected these. But sea anemones, sea cucumbers, and a starfish that closed an eyelid with something resembling a wink, received flattering attention. These specimens gave proof that higher animals can live in the depths.

Some amazing finds have ridden to the surface in dredges or nets. The research ship *Vema*, of Columbia University's Lamont Geological Laboratory, dredged up several specimens of a tiny animal called Neopilina, which had been thought extinct for three hundred million years.

UNDERWATER CAMERA

No one dredge or trawl is satisfactory for catching all types and sizes of organisms, and at best it is difficult to bring up deep-water animals alive or in an undamaged condition. Fish scooped up from the depths undergo terrific changes in pressure. The shock is often fatal to delicate mechanisms, and fish also react violently to changes in temperature. Only a few survive a rough haul.

In the past, see-it-yourself biologists dreamed of the day when they could enter the depths themselves to observe plants and creatures of the sea in their natural surroundings instead of groping blindly from the surface. The aqualung diving equipment developed by Emile Gagnon and Captain Jacques Cousteau turned out to be a boon. With an aqualung to regulate pressure automatically, scientists could stay underwater long enough to observe, photograph or capture marine life.

Seeing the contribution that skin diving might make to all aspects of oceanography, including marine biology, Cousteau bought a craft that had served as a minesweeper during World War II. He equipped the *Calypso* for scientific purposes. Although he was a naval academy trainee rather than a scientist, Cousteau had learned much about the sea during his free diving experiments and also during a preliminary period of marine research while using a vessel owned by the French government.

In the *Calypso* wheelhouse, Cousteau had installed the best available radar gear, gyroscopes and automatic pilot. Two king posts flanking the wheelhouse supported a high observation bridge and searchlight projectors. At the bow he designed an underwater observation chamber eight feet beneath the water line. Below decks, in addition to rooms for crew and staff, he equipped a divers' ready room with air compressors to fill diving lungs and with electric generators for electronic devices and underseas lighting systems.

The lanky Cousteau headed the *Calypso*'s first expedition to the Red Sea in 1951. A small crew with a limited amount of money but a lot of hope proved that skin diving could open up new possibilities in undersea explorations.

To save time locating sites that might merit further research, Cousteau designed an underwater sledge, similar to that invented by other scientists, but with fin and rudder controls so the pilot could move up, down and sideways when towed by a boat in relatively shallow water.

The newest model of these sledges is an electronic submarine scooter with a starter and accelerator on the right-hand grip. By turning his body and fins, a diver can rocket past manta rays looking like twin-engined bombers and Portuguese-men-of-war with tangles of tentacles.

The use of sledges and scooters is limited to marine biologists skilled in the use of aqualungs, but a recent invention opens new possibilities for visual inspection of the depths by untrained divers. The towvane, devised by an Australian named Mac Lawrie, is a heavily constructed vessel with portholes that looks something like a space capsule. The operator is sealed in, lowered overboard and towed by a small surface craft. To dive toward the bottom, the operator depresses the vanes; to rise, he angles them upward and surfaces automatically.

Marine biologists use cameras even more than sledges, scooters or towvanes. Dr. Maurice Ewing, working with Dr. Edward M. Thorndike of Queen's College, New York, evolved a lens which corrected underwater distortion. Cousteau, who eventually resigned from the French Navy to become director of the Oceanographic Museum at Monaco, carried out a number of experiments with underwater photography. Once while he was aboard his research vessel cruising through the Indian Ocean, the *Calypso* hit and injured a whale. Cousteau ordered it shot. Before the whale could be brought aboard the boat, the sinister forms of blue and gray sharks appeared in the water.

"Good chance to film an attack," said Cousteau.

The crew tried to dissuade him from going down into the water with a movie camera, but he insisted that the shark cage would give him protection.

The crew watched anxiously as Cousteau and cameraman Laban descended in the flimsy-looking cage dangling at the end of a cable. From inside the cage, Cousteau and Laban could see the sharks close in for a ten-pound bite of whale. Frustrated because the slats interfered with movie-making, the divers opened the door cautiously. Although horrified by the spectacle, Cousteau leaned out of the cage and filmed away frantically.

Suddenly a shark that had been circling around the whale darted toward the cage. The divers slammed the door shut.

When they surfaced, two more divers went down. A dozen descents in the cage resulted in the shark sequence seen in Cousteau's movie *The Silent World*. This and similar films contributed much both to scientific and popular knowledge of life beneath the waves.

Dissatisfied with the performance of underwater cameras, Cousteau persuaded Dr. Harold Edgerton, member of the staff of the Massachusetts Institute of Technology and inventor of speed-light cameras, to join him on extended *Calypso* cruises. They were backed by the French government and the United States' National Geographic Society. Cousteau and Edgerton made extensive use of cameras they designed themselves while studying the scattering layers that had interfered with submarine detection during World

War II. The question was still being debated as to whether temperature, salinity or living organisms caused them.

Lowering specially designed speed-light cameras into the scattering layers, Edgerton and Cousteau got pictures that showed billions of tiny specks that might be plankton but could be dead tissue. In some shots, clouds of tiny shrimp showed up. Edgerton and Cousteau, aided by depth ships as well as cameras, pursued the subject of the scattering layers for several summers. They came to the conclusion that the sea resembles a great bowl of living soup, with life becoming more abundant at the depths. This theory has been hotly contested by marine biologists, because it goes counter to the long-held assumption that life diminishes with depth.

In 1956 Cousteau and Edgerton became interested in the question of whether creatures can live in the deepest parts of the sea. To find the answer, they sent down cameras from the *Calypso,* hovering over the Romanche Trench off the Ivory Coast of Africa. One morning Edgerton lowered an electronic camera on a cable and bounced it up and down for three hours, hoping that flashes were exploding every quarter minute. When he hauled the camera up, he found that the lens had cracked. Of the hundreds of exposures, only two resulted in clear pictures, but these did show that life existed at great depths.

Such experiments proved the practicality of using cameras in water too deep for towvaners or marine biologists with aqualungs. Marine biologists can now choose from among a wide variety of cameras both manned and unmanned.

Sea cameras must be watertight and rugged; yet some are so delicate that a jellyfish can trip them by passing in front of the photoelectric cell. One type, called the Bathygraph, is automatically pressurized by an aqualung cylinder underneath the camera. It runs on a tiny silver potassium battery. The most unusual of the unmanned cameras are the Halibuts, camera-toting bottom sleds developed by Edgerton and Cousteau.

Cameras, nets, scooters and aqualungs have made it possible for marine biologists to learn a great deal about the effect of environment on creatures of the sea. Diminished light intensity has a marked influence on the coloring of animals of the deeps. Their characteristic pigments are black, dark brown, red, and orange. Because red light disappears after about three hundred feet, red-hued animals are no more visible to their enemies than are their drably colored companions.

As might be expected, continual darkness affects the vision of a number of fish. Blind ones compensate for loss of eyesight with feelers and long, slender fins. Those that have remained sighted often have protruding telescopic eyes.

Some fishes light their way with the help of efficient little torches which they turn on and off at intervals. Marine biologists have discovered that in certain species phosphorescence is only the by-product of a chemical process. A few produce light by discharging a luminous slime. Specific organs called photospheres and combinations of lens and concave reflector formations account for spangles of brightness in others. Fishes use lights to see by, to lure others to them, to detect their own species, or to defend themselves by ejection of luminous clouds.

Marine biologists took little interest in sound production by creatures of the sea until it became a naval problem. Prior to that, tales of early sailors who insisted that white whales made a sort of whistling noise had been looked upon as fanciful.

In 1942, after the United States entered World War II, marine biologists were asked to solve an underwater problem of noise at Chesapeake Bay. Baffling, unidentifiable sounds were so loud that they masked the movement of ships. An underwater listening system set up for submarine detection had been rendered useless. Ship engines, waves and pile driving equipment had always created some interference, but now the overall effect picked up on hydrophones resembled that of pneumatic drills tearing up pavement. The noise level rose at night.

Could the disturbance be coming from finny creatures? naval officials asked marine biologists. After studying the sound effects from regularly spaced hydrophones, the team of scientists agreed that fish might well be the disturbers. If they were, small explosions set off in the water would probably silence them momentarily.

Checking on this theory, marine biologists exploded small charges. After a detonation the noise stopped, but soon began again.

While the experimentation was going on, fishermen reported unusually large quantities of croaker fish, which habitually moved into the Bay from their wintering grounds. When biologists captured some of the fish and transferred them to an aquarium for study, tests confirmed that croakers did indeed make up the Chesapeake Bay chorus. Technicians succeeded in screening out the noise of the croakers by using electric filters.

Intensive studies carried out with echo sounders used in conjunction with cameras have proved that sound production is a common occurrence in fish. Porpoises moo, crabs click, and disgruntled sea bass emit deep-pitched thumps. However, sea noises that create a clamor on a hydrophone may not be audible to the ears of divers. Biologists are uncertain about the function of the sounds. They may be a defense mechanism, or they may bring individuals together for mating and spawning.

Another subject of interest to biologists is how fish get around. Free-swimming fishes are streamlined in such a way that they almost glide through the water. The giant squid is propelled by a unique system of jet propulsion—ejecting water through a funnel-shaped device. Some fishes, like the jellyfish, have bodies encased in thick but fragile gelatinous sheaths. Because the water-saturated tissues have almost the same density as the surrounding ocean, they can maintain their level in the water with balloonlike buoyancy.

Many of the deep sea organisms are drifters. Plankton, too small and too feeble to resist currents, go where the water takes them; zooplankton commute. At night they climb upward but sink downward with the rising of the sun. Their problems of flotation are solved in several ways—by filmy appendages, hairlike arrangements and excretion of oil.

Although marine biologists are interested in how the sea affects life within it, they are more interested in how sea creatures affect man-made objects when they come in contact with them. In more than one instance, marine biologists called upon to explain extensive damage to breakwaters have traced the difficulty to a destructive species of sponge boring into the rock and cement.

Marine biologists are frequently consulted on problems affecting naval efficiency. Could they, from their knowledge of barnacles, develop a new kind of anti-fouling paint? the Navy asked. The biologists could. The paint they suggested reduced the time a ship had to spend in dry dock getting overhauled. Because the paint repelled barnacles, ships had less encumbrance on their surfaces and could increase speed.

While engaged in studies of sponges, barnacles, jellyfish and croakers, marine biologists have learned much about habits and characteristics of dwellers in the depths. Until recently little more was known about crabs than that they nipped the toes of waders. Biologists now know, among other things, that crabs are very nearly omnivorous. One species stalks its prey like leopards. Some are expert swimmers; others are crawlers, burrowers and climbers. Most crabs are slow, but a few race. Active and courageous, crabs are capable of registering anger or alarm. They squabble like human beings over a desirable dwelling.

Fascinating as scientists may find the study of crabs clowning on marine flats, they realize that the biggest contribution marine biology can make is to find out which creatures of the sea are harmless and can be made to serve mankind, and which are a menace.

Studies conducted by marine biologists have exploded many myths. The ancients believed that a manta could wrap its great wings around a man and crush him to death. Biologists now say that despite his spikes and ugliness, the manta is harmless. On the other hand, sea anemones, some of which resemble beautiful dahlias, carry in the cells of their waving arms poison darts that may sting fishermen; fire coral is more of a menace than poison ivy; the red-and-white banded lionfish with long fins and bristling lances can eject a venom that disables its victim.

Marine biologists have a twofold interest in sharks because of their attacks on other fish that might supply food for man and because of their threat to swimmers. The evidence has been confused.

In the past, fishermen hated and feared sharks because they supposedly gulped down human beings as well as seafood. Later, research done by skindivers seemed to indicate that these fish were relatively harmless. But in 1960 there were thirty documented attacks by sharks upon swimmers off both coasts of the United States. Five of the victims died. Why sharks ignore swimmers at some beaches and turn killers at others puzzled scientists and laymen alike. Could marine biologists make any suggestions as to how persons might avoid the man hunting fish or defend themselves in an emergency? The American Institute of Biological Science set up a Shark Research Panel to ferret out the answers.

To aid them they had the benefit of research initiated by the U.S. Navy during World War II. Anxious to gain protection for men who might have to swim in shark-infested waters after a plane's forced landing or a ship's sinking, officials had sought advice from scientists at Woods Hole Oceanographic Institution, who had succeeded in preparing water-soluble wax cakes of copper acetate and nigrosine dye that repelled sharks. Distributed all over the world to men aboard ships, the cakes undoubtedly have saved many lives.

The new Shark Panel concentrated on beach areas instead of the open sea. Research indicated that the shark is a killer or a coward, wily or stupid according to circumstances. In shallows, sharks tend to be most vicious whenever the water temperature is in the seventies or high sixties. However, if hungry enough, sharks will venture into even colder water, and they seem to be hungry much of the time. They eat almost anything in prodigious quantities—including biscuit tins, crates, sacks of coal and alarm clocks. These fish have an incredibly keen sense of smell and are acutely sensitive to sound waves in the water. The kind of vibration may be the explanation for the attack. If vibrations are erratic and irregular, the shark is likely to investigate.

Biologists of the Shark Panel do not belittle the shark as a man-killer, but they do believe the danger can be reduced if a swimmer always has a companion and avoids swimming at night or in turbid water. Panelists advise that a swimmer who sees sharks should try to remain calm and head for shore using strong, regular strokes.

The answers on sharks and other creatures of the sea that scientists have brought up from the depths have an important bearing on the lives of those who live on land, but the biggest question of all —to what extent the creatures of the sea can best serve mankind —is still unanswered. Extensive studies of life in the depths will require better research facilities than we now have.

For scientists, as for other men, the deep ocean has an irresistible fascination, for it is still a virtually unknown world. Marine biologists, aquanauts of the future, intend to make that unknown yield answers that will dispel myths and menaces now presented by dwellers in the depths.

4

Crops from the Sea

Each night millions of people go to bed hungry. In some countries every bit of available land is already under cultivation and is gradually wearing out. Can a population that threatens to triple within the next century turn increasingly to the sea for food? Do fish, seaweed, and plankton provide the necessary vitamins, calories and minerals for strength and growth?

Marine biologists and chemists confronted with such questions are already talking about algae soup, herring bread and seaweed candy. Animal foods taken from the sea total more than thirty million tons annually, but this yield will have to be increased. Obviously, one way to do this is to find out where sea food is most abundant.

When Norwegian scientists and fishermen reported that Marconi echo meters responded to pulse echoes presumably caused by fish, marine biologists got to work on sonar devices. Their experimentation resulted in a Seagraph sounder, which by a hydrophone system, could pick up echoes from schools of fish. These activated an automatic tracer that made graphs or traces on a screen.

Through laboratory studies, biologists discovered that traces vary with different kinds of fish, and large fish produce stronger return signals than small ones; but echo sounding is far from perfect. Mackerel, cod, herring and sprat can usually be identified accurately by the kind of traces they record on the graph, but some species of fish do not produce a consistent, characteristic noise. One fish, because of variations in size or in density of the water, or because of change in depth below the fishing vessel, may give rise to different kinds of traces. Over sand and mud an echo sounder may pick up almost no shrimp noise, but over honeycombed shale the creatures register considerable disturbance.

Even with their drawbacks, the echo sounders save time, money and effort. No traces mean no fish; so, in areas where echo sounders register nothing, fishermen do not waste energy casting. If there are schools of fish, the sounder locates them more quickly than can fishermen depending on chance. Vessels equipped with echo sounding devices usually have a catch three times as large as those without them.

Which species of fish inhabit which parts of the sea remained a conundrum until marine biologists discovered that there are layers of water in the ocean, much like layers of a cake, with characteristic temperature and salinity. Fish show preferences for cool or warm water, also for clear or muddy, and habitually swim at a chosen level. Taking the temperature of the water can give a marine biologist a hint as to what kind of fish may be lurking there.

If the temperature changes drastically, fish migrate. When water off the California coast became warmer, the salmon left, ruining a well developed industry. Celluloid tags attached to the tail or dorsal fins of fish have given proof that they will swim great distances to escape marked changes in movement, salinity or temperature of the water.

Because small plant and animal organisms are sources of food for marine life, a good supply of plankton usually means an abundance of fish. To chart its patterns of distribution marine biologists use various kinds of plankton recorders. One type, hollow and torpedo-shaped, is towed through the sea behind a boat. Water enters at a small opening in the front and strikes a silk gauze moving continually across the incoming stream. Plankton stick to the gauze; the water passes out the rear of the instrument.

Later, in the ship laboratory, a scientist takes the spools out of the plankton recorder, unrolls the gauze and cuts it in squares. He then examines, counts and identifies the preserved organisms. If the speed of the gauze is known as well as the speed and course of the ship, the marine biologist can easily compute the distribution of plankton. From this data, charts are drawn up for the use of fishing vessels. Because zooplankton migrate, the picture is constantly changing.

As an aid to fishermen off the east coast of the United States, scientists who are members of the Atlantic States Marine Fisheries Commission occasionally issue a forecast—"Lobster, Maine only: Good. Oyster in the Chesapeake Bay area: Poor." The forecasts are based on a number of variable factors, including current, water temperature, salinity, spawning rates in known hatching areas, pollution and predator strength. Fish forecasters, like weather forecasters, often qualify their predictions with "probable."

Intensive biological surveys of given areas furnish important clues to the availability of sea food. In recent years, scientists working in the sub-zero cold of the Antarctic have uncovered a treasure chest of animals that crawl, cling and swim in water constantly at the point of freezing. Surprisingly, life is more abundant in these polar regions than anywhere else in the world.

Japan proved dramatically that such things as the Antarctic survey and the use of plankton recorders and echo sounders can have practical results. After World War II, Japanese fishermen were excluded from many of their former fishing grounds, and so, in the early nineteen hundred fifties, the Board of Fisheries began an elaborate campaign to find new sources of sea life. Marine biologists collected data on temperature, salinity, currents, migration and spawning areas. Survey vessels with electronic sounding gear covered miles of ocean searching especially for tuna, usually found far from land and thus in waters unclaimed by any specific nation.

Suspecting that tuna inhabited ocean currents, scientists starting with known concentration of tuna used buoyed lines to follow currents leading from them. They located not only new tuna grounds but also places to dredge for bottom species of fish such as cod and halibut. In 1958 Japanese fishermen had catches exceeding any pre-war year by nine hundred thousand tons.

If fish are to be funneled to markets in increasing quantities it is important not only to locate them but to improve equipment used to catch them. For hundreds of years fishermen cast their nets into the sea hit and miss. Rocky bottoms often damaged them. If nets came up with only a few fish their owners had no way of knowing whether the fish were scarce or the equipment inadequate.

Skin divers and marine biologists with cameras can now supply fishermen with profiles of the depths so that underwater hazards can be avoided. Photographs also show how equipment operates. A film made by Cousteau and Dumas for Mediterranean fishermen showed that the type of nets they used caused fishes to leap away like rabbits running from the reaper, but very different results showed up in a film done by Commander Hodges for the Marine Laboratory of the Scottish Home Department. A sequence of photographs on the action of the Danish seine trawl showed that the towline running ahead stirred up fish from the bottom which then schooled directly in the path and were carried into the deep end of the net. Open meshes allowed young fish to wiggle out, but very few adult ones escaped.

Observations on the behavior of fish when exposed to light led to another new technique for catching them. Marine biologists noted that fish confronted by light went into a sort of shock reaction. They first descended, then rose, then aggregated. Today some fishing vessels attract finny creatures by light, then guide them by an electronic device toward a tube through which they are pumped into the hold.

Marine biologists do more than locate fish and help develop effective equipment for capturing them. They also concern themselves with factors that affect survival. Underwater warfare is savage and unrelenting. Scientists hope to take steps to get rid of the enemies of the fish used for food. Chemical controls that would repel certain species have been suggested. Some scientists believe it might be possible to drag a filtering device along the sea bed and literally weed out unwanted animals. Others believe manatees might be used to chew their hungry way through aquatic weeds. But no practical method has yet been devised. There is also a question of how many animals can be eliminated from an area without upsetting the necessary balance of life.

Crops from the Sea

A crisis in the sardine industry made industrialists and marine biologists alike realize that an understanding of the reproductive processes and life cycles of fish might suggest ways to aid survival. Before 1946 the sardine industry flourished. In addition to canning fish the factories processed oil and prepared fish meal for poultry and stock. Suddenly sardines almost disappeared from waters where they had once teemed. Research showed that of the hundred thousand eggs a sardine spawned in a year a bare one per cent survived. Now under way are various studies on measures that could be taken to decrease infant mortality among sardines and other fishes.

Marine biologists are also exploring possibilities for increasing the supply of fish by transplanting them to a more favorable environment. Plaice transferred from one side of the Dogger Bank in the North Sea to the other have grown twice as rapidly because of improved food supply. Striped bass, shad, and soft shell clams moved from the eastern coast of North America to the Pacific have thrived. Distribution of fish by government hatcheries introduced salmon into Chilean and New Zealand waters.

The most reliable method of increasing the supply of food fishes is through aquaculture. The simplest method is enclosing sea creatures in an inland estuary by building a dike and then providing appropriate food. Shellfish, oysters, and mussels have been successfully cultivated but there is need for huge aquaria or oceanariums with controlled conditions simulating the ocean.

It may be possible to farm the sea itself. Already divers and fishermen are excluded from a section of Monaco Bay where scientists have planted weeds on the ocean floor. Experiments expected to last over a period of years are being carried out there to discover what weeds are most favored by fishes. Marine biologists also expect to find clues as to the most suitable type of fish for breeding in artificial underground grazing grounds.

Sea farming might take the form of planting animals instead of weeds. Researchers of the private Beaudette Foundation for Biological Research have found huge eel grass beds in San Quentin Bay off Baja, California. These once nurtured sea turtles, a major food resource. But the creatures with paddlelike flippers have all been destroyed. Scientists at the Foundation believe that sea turtles could be re-established in the estuary.

Success in sea farming will depend in part on an understanding of the food chain that exists in the sea. Marine biologists have known for a long time that the great fish eat the little ones. Whales gulp down copepods by the barrel. Bottom feeding cod and haddock, forced to subsist on leftovers escaping hungry mouths in the water above them, consider starfish a delicacy. The ocean is full of strange, little-understood alliances in the struggle for survival. While snapping a picture of a big sea bass, photographer Luis Marden of the National Geographic staff saw a fingerling swim close to it. He expected the bass to swallow the tiny fish, but the bass turned its attention to a larger one. The fingerling remained nearby filching the scraps which did not enter the bass's mouth.

Grazers of the sea eat seaweed or various forms of plant and animal plankton. As yet plankton is abundant in most parts of the sea but fishes nourished by it require enormous quantities. If plankton becomes scarce, fish migrate out of an area as cattle amble away from a grazed-out range. Marine biologists hope to find ways of stimulating plant production to feed the grazers among fish.

Fertility seems to be greatest where overturning or upwelling brings an interchange of surface water with bottom water. Water in the depths is rich in nutrients because uneaten plankton and fragments of organic matter settle in the silt at the bottom where bacteria break them into phosphates and nitrates. Layers of stagnant water can keep nutritive materials on the bottom or in a layer of the sea where oxygen is so scarce that most fish would die trying to find food. But currents, convection and wind storms all help to waft the rich minerals aloft so they can be taken up by sea plants and re-enter the food cycle. Fertility is greatest where the bottom water is agitated. Marine biologists have long entertained schemes for stirring the water artificially in sterile parts of the ocean.

At a meeting of the Food and Agriculture Organization of the United Nations in 1961 various plans for pumping or ploughing the oceans were discussed. Some of these sound like science fiction but they do offer possibilities. One suggestion involves use of a nuclear reactor to generate heat on the bottom of the ocean. As the water warmed it would rise, sucking up nutrients with it, which could be distributed by convection currents.

Actually pumping water from the depths would require so much power that the expense would be prohibitive, but there are proposed projects that center around siphon and pump principles. A possibility would be to lower a pipe into the ocean with one end near the bottom, the other near the surface, and then force water through it with a pump. Once started, the water would continue flowing by itself because of the differences in temperature and density between the deep water and the surface water.

Fertility of the ocean might also be increased by adding certain chemicals known to affect plants and animals favorably, but as yet the chemistry of the ocean is only slightly understood. Before water is doctored chemists must find out how fast and by what process bacteria produce nitrates and phosphates. There may be nitrogen-fixing bacteria in plants of the sea as there are in plants on the land. These could be a key element in maintaining fertility.

Marine biologists do not believe aquaculture should be confined to products already popular. They hope to re-educate public taste to accept plants and animals now considered inedible. Americans reject octopus, squid, snails and shark; yet people in the European lands bordering the Mediterranean esteem squid and octopus and make soup of snails. The Chinese regard shark fins as a great delicacy and point out that the flesh of these fish is excellent in texture and flavor. Marine biologists predict that as food shortages become more acute many seafoods now considered unfit may be welcomed on dinner tables.

One scientist, interested in enlarging sources of food supply, boiled animal planktonic organisms, fried them in butter, and served them on toast to a group of friends. His guests, commenting on their shrimplike flavor, considered them a delicacy. Thor Heyerdahl ate plankton on his epic raft trip across the Pacific to test the theory that the original inhabitants of Polynesia might have come from South America on rafts propelled by the Equatorial Current. A person at sea need not starve, Heyerdahl later asserted, if he has a means for straining the water around him.

However, there is a difference between what a man adrift on a raft will eat to survive and what he will eat when he has access to a well-stocked grocery store. Also there is a question as to whether plankton affords much food value or supplies much energy. And even in productive areas a huge volume of water would have to be filtered to get plankton equivalent to a pound of beans. Skeptical scientists think it will take considerable research to determine whether men can exploit plankton; optimistic ones talk in terms of pumps, filters, and factory ships operating much like mechanical whales.

Marine biologists are also exploring the possibilities of using seaweed as a food. Its total tonnage in all the waters of the world is impressive and it grows a crop that could be harvested two or three times a year by boats equipped with underwater cutters. From the fronds of red seaweed, which extracts and concentrates minerals into the liquid of its cells, the Japanese make a dish they call *nori*. One type of seaweed can be boiled or eaten with vinegar. Another is cooked into seaweed candy. However, only the Orientals show any real appreciation for seaweed as a food. Had Japan not turned to the sea for a good part of her sustenance her teeming population, wholly dependent on meager farms, would have starved.

Marine biologists have answered many questions about the sea as a source of food. They have evolved better techniques for the finding and catching of fish. They have made suggestions that, if carried out, would increase both the survival and supply of marine animals. Certainly sea farming provides at least part of the answer to demands for food for expanding populations.

But marine biologists must seek further for answers to how much food will be available and how nourishing it will be. Admittedly sea food is rich in vitamins, iron, calcium and iodine, but how can its lack of calories be offset? On how large a scale can aquaculture be carried out? The sea must be protected against depletion: fishermen eager to capture the fishes most easily netted and yet commanding high prices have already overfished so ruthlessly that haddock, halibut, sturgeon and salmon have disappeared in certain areas.

The answers are coming from laboratories established by marine biologists all over the world. Above and beneath the seas, scientists with seines, nets, echo sounders and plankton recorders seek knowledge of a world still unconquered. Their goal, whether in the tropics or at the poles, is a common one—food for the future.

5

Underseas Canyons, Rivers and Mountains

One day the engineer-inventor Dr. Harold Edgerton was checking electronic flash installations on the depth ship FNRS-3 at the Toulon arsenal. A French military officer strolled up and asked, "Actually, what are you hoping to find in the pictures you take with your shark camera?"

"I don't know," Edgerton replied. Then he added thoughtfully, "If I knew, I wouldn't bother looking."

Curiosity as to what the ocean hides also prompts marine geologists to descend to the floor of the sea. But they have some very practical reasons for exploration. Engineers directing construction of piers, breakwaters or harbor installations turn to marine geologists for information on bedrock before planning foundations. Captains and pilots of oceangoing vessels, especially submarines, need the answers only scientists can provide as to subsurface menaces to ships and lives. Executives in the mineral and petroleum industry request surveys for the gold, oil and other minerals that lie hidden in the sea.

Because the ocean with its problems of pressure and lack of oxygen has been almost as hostile to man as is the moon, marine geologists have had to make most of their observations of the sea floor from the surface. Dredges have been standard equipment ever since the English scientist Sir John Murray, aboard the *Challenger,* proved the existence of an unseen land through fragments dredged up from the Atlantic. Geologists had already speculated on the existence of

49

an Antarctic continent but none had seen it. In the central part of the Atlantic a *Challenger* dredge brought up only rocks of volcanic origin. But in the waters farther south, fragments of glauconite, quartz and granite appeared. Since these are customarily associated with continental land masses Murray reasoned that they must have been carried by icebergs migrating from an Antarctic continent.

Dredging is used less by modern oceanographers than in *Challenger* days. The process is tedious and rocks can tear holes even in bags or nets of link and ring chain mesh. But the technique is useful at times. One new type of dredge is equipped with a sound-producing instrument clamped to the cable three hundred feet above the dredge itself. Signals from this device give depth measurements so rocks can be avoided.

To get samples of the sediment on the ocean floors, marine geologists use grabs and snappers. Most of these resemble a cup or cylinder with spoon-shaped jaws. As the snapper plummets downward on a chain, tension holds the jaws open. As soon as the sampler has taken a bite of sediment, the tension is released and the cup closes automatically.

Sediment traps also aid investigation, but they have drawbacks. If they are left down for some time, drifting kelp may catch on them and form such a heavy drag that a storm at sea will carry them away. Curious fishermen sometimes pull them up. Also, the rope used for the anchor line is likely to fray; yet if wire is substituted, it develops kinks.

Even with the best equipment, the marine geologist is handicapped by having to work from a platform on a vessel subject to rolls and pitches. While grappling he frequently loses expensive gear because it smashes against an unseen rock ledge. Salt water corrodes metal parts and the great pressures of the sea sometimes cause his apparatus to collapse.

Trying to overcome some of the blindness of their groping, marine geologists make extensive use of cameras. One underseas vehicle designed to help marine geologists can pick up samples as it crawls along the ocean floor spying out of its television eyes. The Remote Underwater Manipulator, RUM, developed by the Office of Naval

WRIST   CLAW   ELBOW   TV CAMERA   CABLE DRUM   CONTROL CABLE   ELBOW

RUM Tractor

Research with help from the Scripps Institution of Oceanography, looks much like a one-man band, drum and all, mounted on a tractor with tanklike treads. In front it has an electrically driven arm and hand which open, close, rotate and flex with almost human dexterity.

The unmanned RUM is linked to shore by a cable long enough to permit it to snoop as far as five miles out to sea and to a depth of twenty thousand feet. The cable carries the television signal, telemeter channels and power for RUM's operation, camera, and lights. Sonar equipment guides its progress over the ocean bottom. The ultimate objective of the RUM program is to develop a vehicle capable of performing such underwater duties as observing the sea floor, collecting samples and specimens, and assembling and installing instrumentation on the ocean bottom.

Capable of even more sustained observations are camera-equipped buoys which may remain submerged for months recording currents and taking pictures of their surroundings. When the marine geologist wants to reclaim a buoy of this type, a small charge exploded nearby triggers the ballast-release mechanism and causes the buoy to surface.

Driven by a consuming desire to inspect the ocean floor personally, scientists have for some years experimented with depth ships. In the nineteen thirties Dr. William Beebe invented the bathysphere, a steel diving chamber with portholes for observation. Although he brought back information about a fantastic underseas world, his craft, which had to be tethered to a host vessel, was too rigid, too limited in its range and too much at the mercy of the sea to permit extensive research on the ocean floor.

Later, Swiss-born Auguste Piccard, trained in science and engineering, abandoned his study of cosmic rays via balloon flights when he decided that the ocean depths offered as much of a challenge as outer space. He dreamed of inventing a depth ship, safer and more manageable than the bathysphere, that would penetrate to parts of the sea man had never reached before.

Piccard's first bathyscaphe made the descent successfully but got badly battered when towed. After overcoming innumerable difficulties, the Swiss scientist, with help from his son Jacques, perfected a new bathyscaphe that he called the *Trieste* in honor of the Italian city where it was built. A kind of underwater balloon, the craft had a heavy steel pressure-resisting cabin suspended from a buoyant, gas-filled float. Depth could be adjusted by increasing or decreasing the ballast. Launched August 1, 1953, the *Trieste* soon proved itself in record-breaking dives.

The United States Office of Naval Research saw the possibilities the bathyscaphe offered, not only for studying the transmission of sound, but also for expanding information about the geography and geology of the sea. When the Navy acquired the *Trieste* it also engaged the services of Auguste and Jacques Piccard.

Scientists were eager for the *Trieste* to make a descent into the Challenger Deep in the Marianas Trench area southwest of Guam, then believed to be the deepest spot in all the oceans. On January 23, 1960, the *Trieste* and its host destroyer, the *Lewis,* made the final preparations for the diving operation which had been tagged Project Nekton.

Dr. Andreas Reichnitzer, scientific director of the project, said to Lieutenant Don Walsh, U.S.N., who would make the depth dive with Jacques Piccard, "Son, we have really found you a hole. Now please see one animal down there."

Marine geologists anticipated a report on the topography of the thirty-five thousand foot gash in the ocean floor. If conditions were at all favorable the *Trieste*'s propellers, driven by low-power electric motors, would make it possible for Piccard and Walsh to cruise along close to the bottom.

During the descent the two men had a bad moment when the bathyscaphe rocked as if experiencing an earthquake. Their excitement mounted as the fathometer indicated they had reached a depth never before visited by man. When the landing chain touched the bottom, the *Trieste* balanced in roily water. Because Walsh and Piccard would have to postpone their exploration of the floor until the water cleared, they settled down to observe whatever might be seen out of the Plexiglas windows. Piccard saw a shrimp float by. Peering out of another porthole, Walsh noticed that a series of cracks had appeared in the outer window which at the depth of over six miles had been subjected to pressures of 8.2 tons per square inch.

Because the cracked window was a threat to their safety, Walsh and Piccard had to forego cruising around. Both were disappointed that they had no more to report, but in many ways the exploit had been as momentous a breakthrough as a flight into space. To marine geologists it meant the threshold of a new era in which they could investigate mountains and canyons beneath the waves.

Since the descent of Piccard and Walsh into the Challenger Deep, much precise scientific research has been carried out by the *Trieste* and bathyscaphes of other nations. Oceanographer Cousteau, although pleased with his French-sponsored depth ship *FNRS-3*, saw the need for underwater craft with more maneuverability and versatility than the bathyscaphes. Assisted by engineer constructor Jean Mallard, he built a peewee depth ship nicknamed *The Turtle*. A small, two-man, free-operating submarine with a forged steel hull, it can go up, down, right or left, propelled by jets of water spewed out by an electric pump. Inside the steel hull a pilot and an observer lie on their stomachs on a rubber mattress while peering out Plexiglas ports. Their equipment includes a gyrocompass, a telephone, electro-sounding gear and cinécameras.

From data accumulated by miniature submarines, depth ships, dredges and cameras, marine geologists are beginning to have a clearer picture of the ocean floor. On their topographic maps they can now fill in, with some degree of accuracy, details on continental shelves. The International Committee on Nomenclature of Ocean Bottom Features defines these as the zone around continents extending from low water line to the depth at which there is a marked increase of slope to greater depth.

More is known about these areas than about most of the ocean because the average depth of the water above them is within the limit of aqualung diving experts. Discovery of oil-bearing formations on some of the shelves has spurred interest in research.

Continental shelves may be large enough to extend under whole seas like the Baltic, or there may be none at all, as along the eastern coast of Formosa. Scoured by waves, tides and currents, the continental shelf is a battleground in the ceaseless war between sea and land. It can be composed of anything from sand and silt to clay and rock. Because sunlight penetrates into all but the deepest part of the shelf, marine plants grow in the waters above it, and seaweed clings to its rocks. Beyond the continental shelf the seascape becomes more stark.

The ocean bottom beyond the shelf resembles a plain, but a plain marked by ridges and troughs. It was once believed that if a motorist could drive along the ocean floor from New York to Ireland, he could do so without changing gears, but marine geologists now know that the bottom of the sea is far from smooth.

Deep sea research ships tracking patiently back and forth across the oceans have found underseas mountains with towering peaks and sheer cliffs more rugged than anything land can boast. In 1954 Soviet scientists detected a two-mile-high ridge beneath Arctic ice and named the mountains Lomonov in honor of a Russian poet.

Later, a Lamont Geological Observatory research team headed by Dr. Maurice Ewing discovered a globe-girdling chain of underwater ridges meandering down the length of the north and south

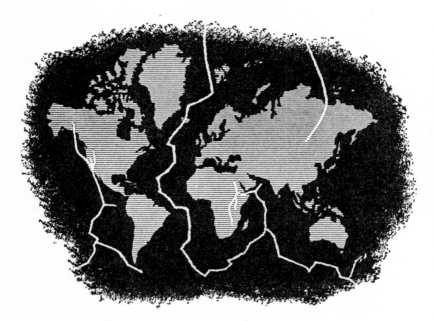

THE CRACK IN THE OCEAN FLOOR

Atlantic, passing around Antarctica and into the Pacific. At intervals islands such as the Hawaiian chain perch on the peaks of these underseas mountains.

Origins of the forty thousand mile long chain of mountains baffled marine geologists. Had some relentless force pushed upward against the floor of the sea, or had these mountains once rested on land which had sunk beneath the waves? And what accounted for the huge, mysterious crack running down the middle of the ridges? Was the earth splitting apart?

Marine geologists from Lamont undertook a study of the rifts of the Pacific. They suspected that they might show abnormally high temperatures because sub-sea earthquakes tend to occur along the ridges. Thermograds, lowered to the bottom of the ocean, confirmed this belief. From studies with these and other instruments, the Lamont scientists theorized that the earth is slowly warming up, expanding, and cracking its crust.

Besides the central, continuous mountain range, the floor of the Pacific is littered with isolated mounts that rise like huge cones from the ocean floor. These guyots, as geologists call them, have smooth-planed tops often garlanded with long-dead coral reefs. Marine geologists believe the mounts to be extinct volcanoes. But how did they get there?

Another ocean bottom problem that fascinates oceanographers is the origin of the deep troughs that are found mostly in the Pacific. Were they caused by the action of turbidity currents, rivers, or earthquakes? Whatever the force, it must have been a powerful one. The Tonga Trench between New Zealand and Samoa could hold seven Grand Canyons in its abyss. All the trenches under the Pacific seem to be uneasy parts of the earth's crust. Because deep-focus earthquakes rumble out of them and fiery volcanoes spout upward on the landward side, oceanographers call these trenches the Pacific ring of fire.

Earth's mightiest rivers flow under the sea. They have neither source nor mouth. For the most part their direction is unknown.

Accumulating data on rivers, mountains, and other features of the ocean floor has been far from simple, even with the help of depth ships, cameras, and *Turtles*. Because of a permanent sheet of ice, the difficulties in the Arctic have been enormous. Marine geologists have, however, been aided by the findings of instruments riding Navy submarines. In 1958 the atomic-powered *Nautilus,* equipped with a battery of scientific gadgets, nosed its way under a canopy of jagged blocks of ice from Point Barrow, Alaska, to Spitzbergen in the Greenland Sea. Its Fathometer shot electrical impulses to the ocean floor, automatically registering the pinging echoes that bounced back. The resultant graph revealed soaring sea mounts and deep valleys.

At times, sandwiched between the ocean floor and ice protruding downward from above, the *Nautilus* seemed doomed. But it amassed important information. One of the discoveries of the crew was an island nine hundred feet below the icy surface of the Arctic.

Laboratory scientists from the Lamont Geological Laboratory later explored the submerged ice island sighted by the *Nautilus* and found it to be larger than the state of Maryland. The scientific team found almost no life on the floor of the ocean in that area, but on the island they photographed sponges, shrimp, small fish and sea anemones.

Knowledge accumulated on underseas mountains and trenches has been a substantial aid to navigators. Equipped with charts compiled by marine geologists, pilots of ships speed across the water and nose into distant harbors confident that they can avoid turbulent depths and tricky shallows. Contour maps give submarines, even if submerged for days, an accurate idea of where they are, and permit accurate launching of underwater missiles. The findings of marine geologists also contribute to construction of jetties and other man-made coastal structures.

Since the first really large-scale attempt to use modern oceanographic instruments in the exploration of the ocean floor in 1947, when the Swedish scientists manned the *Albatross*, marine geology has made substantial progress. But only a small percentage of the sea floor has been surveyed. The depths still conceal the secrets of the origin of trenches and guyots; underseas canyons and mountains remain unexplored; scientists do not agree on the explanations of an ocean floor cracking apart at its seams or of a ring of fire spewing forth destruction.

To wrest answers from this limitless realm below earth's visible surfaces marine geologists need improved techniques for groping and probing, but most of all they need skill, patience and courage.

6

Digging Holes in the Ocean Floor

Marine geologists, not content simply to study the floor of the sea, are poking holes in it to find out what lies beneath. For removing samples of rock, fossils and sediments from beneath the ocean, scientists use corers, long pipes driven into the ocean bottom by ingenious piston and weight combinations that build up hydrostatic pressure. The corer, weighted on top, bores into the ocean floor much as an apple corer sinks into fruit. It sucks up a sediment core many feet in length. Usually it is placed in a tube for future study in a land-based laboratory.

Future diagnosis of the ocean's sub-basement rocks is expected to provide valuable information on radioactivity, earthquake waves and the earth's internal fires. Fossils brought up in cores will reveal much of the history of our planet. There is also the possibility that valuable resources lie smothered by sediment. Already marine geologists have located deposits of oil.

Bringing up samples from beneath the bed of the sea may be both exciting and hazardous. New Year's Day 1953 the *Horizon* and the *Spencer F. Baird,* sponsored by the Scripps Institution of Oceanography, were over the more than six-mile-deep Tonga Trench gashing the ocean floor between New Zealand and Samoa. This area, with its rocky chasms and fringes of coral atolls, is of particular interest to scientists because of the frequency of earthquakes and volcanoes. Scripps oceanographers hoped that their research might give explanations for the region's instability.

Eager to make a try for a core, the *Baird* crew, tense and expectant, began preparations before daylight. Part of the crew undertook the long-drawn-out preparations involved in lowering the miles of coring pipe by winch. Another team of scientists compiled data from temperature readings and water samples, and conducted seismic shots.

Seismic shooting is a technique for charting strata below the sea by inducing artificial earthquakes. While one ship drops "firecrackers"—depth charges—the second ship listens and observes the electrical fluctuations on an oscillograph. Seismic shooting requires split-second timing.

Baird scientists fused, lighted, and dropped successive charges of TNT into the water. One member of the team checked the shots; another recorded depths. For the benefit of geologists aboard the *Horizon* who would study the recording of sound waves, the *Baird* radio operator transmitted on the intercom such messages as "Three pounder. Estimated burning time of fuse thirty seconds. One minute warning. NOW."

As soon as the TNT hit the surface, noise from the explosion traveled down toward the bottom. Aboard the *Horizon,* where monitors listened in absolute silence, the reflected and refracted sea waves were recorded on the oscillograph. Marine geologists and geophysicists on the *Horizon* already knew how sound behaves in layers of different density. By mathematical calculations based on arrival time and patterns of the sound waves, they estimated the density and thickness of layers of sediments and rock beneath the floor of the Tonga Trench. They could not, however, determine the exact nature of the rock.

All morning long the scientists on the *Baird* worked to the accompaniment of dynamite blasts, the chatter of broadcasters using the inter-com between the vessels, the whine and clatter of the winch slowly lowering the long coring pipes into the Tonga Trench.

A crisis developed when miles of cable fouled so that the wire supporting the corer, which had almost reached the bottom, would go neither up nor down. Crew members peered anxiously at the cable, then at storm clouds massing overhead. If a storm should twist the cable, the tons of weight attached to it could drag the A-frame and fantail of the *Baird* down into the black, cold depths of the Tonga Trench.

By careful maneuvering the crew got the cable unsnarled so that they could begin recoiling it, but they had rewound only eighty meters of it when someone called in an agonized voice, "Hold it!"

All the men except those recording important seismic tests data rushed to the fantail. The wire had kinked. For a moment the scientists thought only of the failure in the work they had been sent to do; then they realized the danger of their situation. If the cable snapped, it could whip across the deck like a lethal snake, killing the men operating the winch.

The crew worked frantically with clamps and weights to remove the kinks, then slowly rewound the wire. At 2:30 A.M. when they finally succeeded in bringing the coring apparatus aboard, most of the scientists had had no sleep for twenty-four hours. At their feet lay a badly damaged coring tube and lead weight, but the core was intact. From study of this sample and others brought up later, marine geologists gained a more complete picture of the ocean's sub-basement. Alternate layers of sediment, rock, volcanic ash, fossilized plants and animals gave clues to gigantic stresses that had gone into the making of that sea floor—weather, glacial action and volcanic eruptions.

From seismic studies came reports of a major discontinuity of sound, occurring sometimes at a depth of about three miles below the bottom of the ocean, sometimes at much greater depths. Above and below what seemed to be a definite line or break, sound waves traveled at a different speed.

Years before, related studies had been made by Andrija Mohorovicic, a Yugoslavian geologist and seismologist. Mohorovicic believed that there might be a definite discontinuity between the earth's rocky outer crust and its mantle, composed possibly of homogenized rocks. His observations on the behavior of earthquake waves at various levels proved his hunch to be true. Scientists began calling the break the "Mohorovicic discontinuity," or the "Moho."

For years marine geologists discussed the question that might be answered if they could penetrate the Moho. A direct sampling of mantle materials lying just below it would throw light on the age, beginnings, formation and history of the earth. Also, fossils found in core samples would reveal steps in the evolution of plants and animals. But the idea of drilling down to the mantle seemed fantastic. To reach it, a corer would have to bite through twenty or thirty miles of the earth's rocky crust, and it would have to be capable of withstanding tremendous heat and pressure. However, the idea looked a little more feasible after echo sounding devices indicated that the Moho lay less deeply buried under water than under land. In some places it extended up to within about three miles of the ocean floor.

Dr. Walter Munk, professor of oceanography at Scripps, and Dr. Harry Hess, professor of geology at Princeton University, roughed out a bold scheme for boring a hole to the Mohole and presented their plan at a meeting of the American Miscellaneous Society, or AMSOC. This group, so-named by its scientist-members as a spoof on scientific and governmental alphabet agencies, has no constitution, no officers, no set membership, and no agenda except take-offs that might include such items as how to tow Arctic icebergs to California for irrigation purposes. But at the AMSOC breakfast where Munk and Hess appeared, the scientists present—especially the marine geologists and geophysicists—expressed enthusiasm for a project to drill holes into the ocean bottom.

AMSOC scientists dubbed their plan Project Mohole and elected Gordon Lill, chief of the geophysics branch of the Office of Naval Research, as their chairman. At the September, 1957, meeting of the International Union of Geodesy and Geophysics in Toronto, the United States representatives introduced the AMSOC daydream. They urged all nations with drilling experience and equipment to consider setting up a Mohole project. The Soviet Academy of Sciences indicated that it would move immediately on such a project.

This spurred AMSOC to seek official status and raise funds for Mohole drilling. The National Academy of Science launched a drive for financial backing. The Office of Naval Research offered sponsorship, and the National Science Foundation made thirty thousand dollars available to Columbia University's Lamont Geological Observatory for survey purposes. A four-ship expedition led by the Lamont Observatory ship *Vema* set off to seek sites free from strong currents and stormy weather where the mantle underlying Moho could be reached easily.

Oil companies became interested in Project Mohole for several reasons. The drilling techniques used might be applicable to the petroleum industry and might also be the means of locating new under-the-ocean-bed deposits of petroleum. Furthermore, equipment employed for Mohole could later be converted to use for offshore oil wells. Company officials offered to pool their finances and industrial know-how with the hard-won knowledge of scientists to draw up plans for an experimental drilling boat. General Motors pledged diesel-electric equipment.

Marine and mining geologists, geophysicists and engineers designed a vessel adapted for Mohole operations. Initials from the sponsoring oil companies—Continental, Union, Shell, and Superior—supplied the craft's name *Cuss I.* For preliminary experimentation, which would involve deep drilling but not a penetration to the Moho, the scientists decided to work off the California coast. Willard Bascom, of the National Academy of Sciences, had already been named technical director of the project.

In March, 1961, the squat, gray *Cuss I,* described by one reporter as "the most unlikely looking vessel since the Jumblies took to sea in a sieve," was towed out of San Diego Harbor. A ninety-eight foot derrick straddled the open well located amidships. So much public interest had been aroused in Project Mohole that *Life* magazine had sent a photographer to cover the test drilling. Author John Steinbeck, an ardent amateur oceanographer, joined the team of scientists which included Willard Bascom, Gordon Lill, Roger Revelle and other competent geophysicists, geologists and seismologists, all of whom were doers as well as thinkers. Paleontologist William Riedel was chief scientist of the expedition.

Over the site selected for the drilling hole, the pilot kept the barge centered by working a wheel and a joy stick that adjusted speed and direction of four outboard motors and propellers. For guidance he

PROJECT MOHOLE

watched a screen recording blips coming from sonar and radar buoys surrounding *Cuss I*. The pilot had an important responsibility. If the barge moved off-center while a coring pipe was down, it might snap the corer, and the pipe's recoil would jolt the craft and endanger the crew.

As scientists needed them, coring pipes arrived on the conveyer belt and were eased by a hoist down a center well through a funnel-shaped guide shoe. As each section of pipe was lowered toward the mud of the San Diego Trough another was screwed into the top of the preceding section. The diamond-studded nose of the drill went down first. Casing and cable followed as the drill crew lifted and pushed in unison as precisely as a ballet corps.

During the first coring test the drill stopped turning. "A break in the shaft," someone croaked hoarsely above the roar of motors, engines and dynamos. For some moments it looked as if the fifteen-million-dollar Mohole Project was doomed; but by the same toil, time, and ingenuity that had carried the project thus far, crewmen salvaged the core, although they lost an expensive diamond drill in the process.

From the location off the California coast *Cuss I* moved to a site off Guadalupe Island near a high mountain fringed by conifers. Working long shifts, the crew had little time for sleep. When they did doze off, any change of sound from the engines or drill rigs aroused them. Aside from their coring activities, scientists busied themselves measuring sound velocity and the temperatures and density of the water. Currents were checked at four levels simultaneously. Geologists recorded all the data in geophysical log books.

When the first core came up, jubilant scientists crowded around. It was gray-green in color, and full of fossils and volcanic ash. Additional samples were not easily obtained. Once a corer was lost when the cable sent down to retrieve it kinked and came up in tortured twists, and operators had to begin all over again. Even when the coring mechanism operated perfectly, it took hours or days for the corer to reach the bottom and bore into it.

The most valuable core taken off Guadalupe was of stark blue basalt brought up from a depth of 601 feet below 11,700 feet of water. Removing extrusions of tiny crystals and placing them in vials, the scientists then gently eased the core into a plastic tube for future study in the laboratory.

Author Steinbeck was so excited by the routines of *Cuss I* that he had almost no sleep for five days. When the basalt core came aboard, he felt joy which he described as "like a great light." He later wrote vividly of the team play required in the *Cuss I* type of exploration. "We'll be all right, with men like these," he commented.

The *Cuss I* expedition proved the coring operation technically feasible and scientifically sound, but for the scientists aboard, fishing up the sub-basement samples was only the beginning of their project. Ahead of them lay hours of tedious, lonely research to read the message of the cores. The specimens ranged in age from ten to thirty million years old, they found. Layers of volcanic ash told the story of eruptions in or under the seas and the remains of animals buried in the successive layers showed changes undergone by various species and indicated that climatic fluctuations had raised and lowered the temperature of the sea.

While ocean-going Mohole scientists supervised the bringing up of cores, land-based geologists concentrated on improving devices that could help them map the contours of materials beneath the ocean floor. Dr. Harold Edgerton came to their assistance with an electrically powered sound ranging device which he called a "thumper." The periodic, low-frequency thump that the gadget emits goes out in all directions at once and penetrates far deeper than the delicate pings of conventional echo sounders.

An experimental thumper used during a cruise of the Woods Hole vessel *Chain* penetrated several kilometers into the sea bottom, and the intensity and pattern of its echoes gave an idea of the profile of layers of the earth's crust hidden from view. Dr. Edgerton set to work devising more powerful instruments that would eventually probe to greater depths and indicate good sites for drilling; and scientists looked forward to drilling a path clear to the Moho in a short time. Such cores, reaching back to the primeval ooze where life began on the earth, can serve as history books for all time. Oceanographers hope to find out more about the origin and composition of the earth. They want to know the exact age of the major ocean basins. Are the continents moving? Is the earth heating or cooling? Somehow, someday, by studying the oceans and what lies buried beneath them, men will find answers to at least some of the questions that have been asked through the centuries.

Secretly, Mohole scientists hope for scientific surprises, for unpredicted discoveries which upset accepted theories are the most valuable result of scientific research. Whatever the results may be, the imaginative men who dreamed, planned and fought for the Mohole Project have opened the way to the exploration of a whole new world.

7

The Restless Earth

Shortly before noon on September 1, 1923, residents in the Japanese cities of Tokyo and Yokohama heard thunderous crashes. Buildings lurched and pitched as if buffeted by choppy waves. Piercing the rumble of crashing bricks came cries of *"Jishin!* Earthquake!"

Moments later most of the city of Yokohama and much of Tokyo lay in ruins. In congested areas many people were crushed or suffocated under the debris of fragile, jammed-together structures. Charcoal braziers, lighted to prepare noonday meals, got out of control and set off a terrifying conflagration. Because the water mains had burst, the firemen could do little to combat the flames which in one area incinerated thirty thousand persons.

A creek used as anchorage for sampans closed as if stitched together and trapped people aboard their vessels. In the coastal region a tidal wave, or *tsunami,* precipitated by the quake drowned additional thousands. All told, one hundred and fifty thousand suffered injuries. In the two stricken cities shrouded by black smoke, a million persons were left with no food, no home and no clothes except the ones they had been wearing when the earthquake struck. It was one of the most destructive ones ever recorded, but each year many areas suffer from shocks of varying degrees of violence, which cause widespread human misery.

Geologists seeking to prevent such disasters through research on the causes, characteristics and effects of earthquakes are called seismologists. In common with other scientists studying subsurface features they have been handicapped by the inaccessibility of the earth below, and must rely mainly on instruments to get their information.

A seismometer utilizes the principle of inertia, the natural tendency of a heavy body to stay put; and the simplest type of instrument consists of a weight hanging from a flexible support. The weight tends to lag behind when the support is moved. Records of earthquakes may be obtained on relatively inexpensive equipment located in an ordinary basement; but there are also elaborate seismometers, so sensitive that to keep them from picking up local or man-made disturbances or from being jiggled too violently by a quake, they are mounted on a rock foundation or on pillars reaching down to bedrock. At the Harvard University Seismological Station, a battery of equipment is housed in a room blasted out of solid rock below the surface of the ground.

Any earthquake, even a minor one, sends out several different kinds of waves. Although seismologists disagree on the designation or characteristics of these, they do agree that there are two types —surface and subsurface. Subsurface ones are usually described as the P and S waves. P waves, often referred to as push and pull waves, are similar to the vibrations set up in the air by sound. Their force is relayed in much the same way as in a rod struck by a hammer. Transverse or S waves, sometimes known as shake waves, travel in exactly the same way waves course down a taut rope fastened at one end and shaken at the other.

To judge the strength of an earthquake, seismologists watch the graph on the seismometer which magnifies the waves and records them on a motor-driven drum with an apparatus for tracing up-and-down lines. If the quake is small the squiggles are tiny. P waves always arrive first. These travel so rapidly that an earthquake in New Zealand may be recorded in Great Britain about twenty minutes later. The farther a seismometer is from the earthquake center, the longer the time spread between the arrival of the P and S waves. If the seismologist, knowing the difference in travel time between the P and S waves, has data from two or more observatories some distance apart, he can use trigonometry to pin-point the place where the earthquake originated. A standard method of locating earthquakes is swinging arcs over globes. Seismologists then measure the distance from each reporting station to the probable tremor area and come up with a series of arcs that represent the actual center, or epicenter.

Some laboratories have additional equipment used for specialized studies of significant earthquakes. A problem has been that quakes come and go very quickly. Seismologists, absorbed in other experiments, have sometimes missed the change in a graph reading and so failed to get the special equipment activated. To cope with such emergencies, Dr. Hugo Benioff of the seismological laboratory of the California Institute of Technology devised a seismograph with an automatic glass pen recorder. An automobile horn attached to the pen honks automatically when a sizeable quake is recorded.

Although slight bobbles in the graphs indicate only a minor disturbance, seismologists sometimes try to trace waves to their origin because they want to learn all they can about the characteristics of waves. Seismologist the Reverend J. Joseph Lynch, working in a laboratory at Fordham University, was once baffled by upturns in his seismograph occurring at twenty-second intervals. He was surprised to find that they originated with children rehearsing a Maypole dance on the campus. Their routines called for stamping in unison three times a minute.

Another time the seismograph registered an undecipherable maze of lines. "This must be a quake to end all quakes," thought the Reverend Lynch, but his investigation revealed that spiders had somehow gotten into his supposedly sealed instruments.

There are now seismographs which separate quakes from local confusion, thereby eliminating jumbles of small, unimportant tracings and recording sharp, large, clear ones. There are electromagnetic seismometers, and extensometers which record strains in subsurface rocks rather than ground displacements. And there are rocket-shaped seismographs that can be lowered to the floor of the ocean to record quakes there. But even with the help of numerous instruments, the data on a specific earthquake may be scanty.

Sometimes seismologists appeal via press and radio to persons living in the affected area to send facts to their laboratories on the time, duration and direction of movement as shown by the swinging of suspended objects, such as pictures, and the direction of overthrow of loose objects such as vases, as well as the nature of earthquake sounds, if any.

In New Zealand, where earthquakes are frequent, the Seismological Observatory has a network of voluntary observers including postal officials, lighthouse keepers and housewives. To guide them in reporting, the amateur observers have Mercalli Scales, which list effects in homely terms and give twelve degrees of shock ranging from "1, Not felt," to "12, Damage total." On the basis of reports from the public and from seismographs, the scientists plot intensities on a map of the district involved.

Seismologists do not spend all their time on charts and in laboratories. Whenever possible they visit quake areas to study after-effects. One group in 1946 spent twenty-five days under primitive conditions studying the results of a quake in the Peruvian Andes.

Teams of scientists in Peru and elsewhere have found dramatic evidence of the violence of the earth's movements. In most earthquake areas, there are apparent faults—places where the earth has been wrenched so that there is a fracture, displacement, or slippage. Sometimes land on one side of a fault is jerked in one direction while land on the other side is moved in the opposite direction. A 1931 quake in New Zealand set fences six feet out of position.

Geologists also study and report upon areas in which topography has been dramatically altered by a quake, such as the 1957 disaster in the Yellowstone Park area. On the night of August 17 a gigantic earthquake sent tons of earth cascading down the Madison River, killing twenty-eight campers. Later, park rangers and geologists, including seismologists, discovered that Secret Valley had disgorged a mud slide that had come down the mountain and spread into the forest. Just outside the park boundaries, the Madison River had backed up behind wrenched-up earth and formed a lake almost three and a half miles long.

Seismologists also visit stricken cities to observe the effects of earthquakes on streets, waterworks, gas pipes and buildings. While making reports on the Japanese quake of 1923 the late Dr. T. A. Jaggar, then head of the Hawaiian Volcano Observatory, lived in a tent and shared mess with the Marines. Visiting jolted cities over a period of years, Jaggar and other seismologists came to the grim conclusion that most injuries and loss of life resulted not from

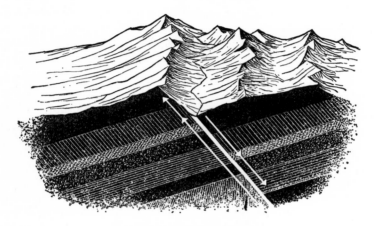

A GEOLOGICAL FAULT

the quake itself but from the collapse of man-made structures. Earthquake-proof buildings could have saved lives, so scientists and a few interested architects set about to determine how a building could be made quake-proof. In addition to collecting eye-witness observations in quake areas, seismologists carried on laboratory tests. At the California Institute of Technology, they built miniature skyscrapers and put them on shocking tables to discover what happens in a real quake.

From their combined field and laboratory studies, seismologists have reached a number of conclusions. They highly recommend reinforced concrete for public buildings. In the Japanese disaster of 1923 only ten per cent of the concrete structures collapsed, but fifty-four per cent of the brick ones were badly damaged. For

73

private homes, seismologists favor wood because of its resiliency. Bricks often separate in a kind of x pattern.

The Long Beach earthquake of 1933 alerted seismologists and architects alike to the vulnerability of buildings with many windows and large, unbraced floor spans. Some new-type schools showed severe damage. Had the quake come during the school day, the death toll would have been appalling. Seismologists recommended that in the future more use should be made of reinforced concrete with horizontal bracing.

Proof that properly constructed buildings can lessen the death toll came at Concepcion, Chile, in 1960. Structures that survived the earthquake had been built along the lines suggested by seismologists.

Terrain makes a great difference in the strain to which a building is subjected. Seismologists report that rock is a better foundation than some types of soft ground, but sand is good because it tends to damp down and extinguish vibrations.

When planning the Imperial Hotel in Tokyo, architect Frank Lloyd Wright studied seismological principles carefully. To give flexibility to the low building of reinforced concrete, he built it in twelve sections and floated it on mud, which served as a cushion. Structures all around it toppled in the 1923 quake; the Imperial Hotel not only stood but became a haven of safety.

Despite knowledge of preventive measures, seismologists have difficulty influencing authorities to lay down codes regarding earthquake requirements for buildings except in the period immediately following tremors. However, seismologists are being consulted more and more about earthquake-proof dams, bridges and water towers, as well as dwellings and factories. A new field, engineering seismology, is attracting some young scientists.

Although seismologists devote much effort to minimizing the effects of earthquakes, they also study causes. To nonscientists the analysis of causes may seem futile, since earthquakes cannot be prevented, but data gained in such studies is useful for predicting possible danger. Seismologists, discouraged by the slowness of such research, sometimes feel that they know little more about quakes than the primitive peoples who thought they were caused by the movements of a gigantic animal imprisoned in the earth. But persistent efforts have yielded many answers.

It is now known that an explosion, landslide, or collapse of a cavern may set off light local shocks. Sometimes the action of a volcano produces tremors. Earthquakes have also been known to result from heavy rainfall or from changes in atmospheric pressure. Most, however, originate far underground.

The earth is never still. Because it rotates at a tremendous speed, its crust is constantly trembling like the rim of a badly balanced flywheel, and nature incessantly remodels it. Rocks disintegrate, move, and gradually build up stresses and strains. Although rocks have some elasticity, the stresses may exceed it. When an unknown force acts as a last straw, rocks slide, rebound, or snap along lines of weakness to release the strain, and the earth is riven sometimes at the surface, sometimes below. Friction and movement trigger vibrations that are transmitted through the earth with tremendous force. A quake in Assam, India, in 1950 had the energy of one hundred thousand average atomic bombs.

From their investigations of faults and forces, certain facts have emerged which help seismologists to predict the possible location and severity of earthquakes. They are likely to recur over old faults such as the San Andreas Fault which originates in Mexico, travels northward underneath California, and then runs out under the Pacific Ocean. An earthquake is most severe at the point where the slippage occurs, which is called the focus or epicenter. The intensity of a quake at any one place depends on the distance from the focus, the depth, and the nature of dislocation. The degree of destruction is determined by such factors as concentration of population, elasticity of terrain, and the presence or absence of huge pounding waves, which often accompany quakes.

Believing they had enough knowledge of causes and effects to be able to forecast earthquakes with some degree of accuracy, seismologists wanted to establish chains of stations that would send out warnings; but no one else seemed much interested. A tidal wave that hit Hawaii in 1946 helped clear the way.

What the public calls a tidal wave scientists call a seismic wave or *tsunami*—from a Japanese word meaning large waves in harbors. So-called tidal waves have nothing to do with tides. Many are the result of earthquakes in the deep trenches of the ocean floor. Water struck by a titanic force rushes into the trenches from all sides, then heaps up, causing waves to move out in all directions. Although they travel up to speeds of five hundred miles per hour, the waves may be only a few feet high, but as the waters approach the shore they pile up ominously.

Before 1946 seismologists had had reports of waves as high as ninety feet, but lacked scientific accounts of their behavior. They could not answer the question as to whether, if a tsunami warning system existed, it would actually save lives.

In the spring of 1946 Francis P. Shepard, professor of submarine geology at the Scripps Institution of Oceanography, was vacationing with his wife in a rented beach cottage on the island of Oahu. On the morning of April 1, Shepard was wakened by a loud, hissing sound. Rushing to a front window he saw roily, angry water where the beach was supposed to be. Then suddenly the water retreated rapidly, leaving the usually invisible coral reefs exposed. Farther up the beach, natives were running out to gather up stranded fish. Thinking all this provided excellent pictorial material, Shepard ran to get his camera and then stationed himself on a ridge in front of the cottage. As he aimed his camera he realized that water was racing toward him with amazing velocity. "Run!" he shouted to his wife.

The Shepards were pursued by a monstrous wall of water which flattened cane fields and swept houses aside. After the tsunami had spent itself, the couple found some of their belongings in the half-destroyed cottage littered with sand and debris. Many of the natives were less fortunate.

Shepard and several other scientists who were also vacationing in the Hawaiian Islands were shocked at the aftermath of damage and death, realizing that if the natives had known that tsunamis retreat only to advance with greater fury, they would not have drowned while trying to pick up scattered fish. As a result, the scientists and a few interested seismologists pooled their experiences, resources, and time to study the cause and origin of tsunamis.

The tsunami to which Shepard had been an eyewitness had originated with a subterranean earthquake off the coast of the Aleutian Islands. If a network of seismological stations had existed, a warning could have been relayed. During the five hours that had elapsed between the quake readings registered at the Alaskan station and the arrival of the tsunami off the coast of Hawaii, civil defense units could have evacuated people from the beaches.

Hammering away at how forewarnings might cut down casualties, seismologists succeeded in getting appropriations to establish a network of stations stretching from Kodiak to Pago Pago. If huge waves appeared, or a sizeable earthquake was registered at one station in the chain, warnings went out to the others. Seismologists could not predict the height of the tsunami, but they could predict the approximate time of arrival. Coastlines could then be evacuated and vehicles, cattle, and mobile possessions could be taken inland. A few times warnings went out that did not eventuate in cataclysmic waves, but in 1957 a destructive tsunami arrived in Hawaii almost on the minute predicted. The property damage matched that of 1946, but not one native lost his life.

Few stations have continual watchers, but at those operated by the U.S. Coast and Geodetic Survey an audible alarm system calls attention to quake readings. Eager to increase the number of stations but faced by shortages of funds and personnel, seismologists have recently been experimenting with unmanned stations. The University of California is pioneering with six of these, located in central California. With telemeter equipment sending automatic reports to the Berkeley campus, the seismologists can locate the epicenter of a small quake within one or two hours after the main shock. If the disturbance seems worthy of study, mobile seismograph units are sent out to do detailed research.

During the few years it has had the status of a science, seismology has provided many valuable answers to engineers, city planners and architects. Damage to waterworks, dams, dwellings and public buildings has been minimized whenever seismological advice has been followed. Property losses would be further reduced if persons would heed seismologists' suggestions to avoid building in vicinities with known faults and build beach homes at a moderate elevation above sea level.

But seismologists face many unanswered questions. They do not agree among themselves on the causes of quakes and tsunamis; there is still no sure way of telling whether sea waves powered by quakes will be negligible or enormous; no one has yet determined exactly how underground stresses and strains develop, and there is no reliable way for predicting much in advance the when or where of an earthquake. Seismological stations are not close enough together to pick up underground warnings and relay them. With population explosions creating larger and larger concentrations of population, the need for earthquake alerts and protective measures will become more important.

An encouraging forward step was the announcement in June, 1960, that the United States planned to provide modern seismological equipment to a hundred and twenty-five stations throughout the world. The only obligations of seismologists in the nations involved would be to send out warnings and to forward data on the nature, location and frequency of earthquakes in their area to the analysis center of the United States Coast and Geodetic Survey in Washington, D.C. The results compiled are made available to researchers of all countries.

A world-wide network of stations will not remove all the obstacles from the path of seismologists, but for scientists, obstacles are a stimulus to further study. International sharing will undoubtedly upgrade seismic research. With the whole underworld as their laboratory and with a shared knowledge of it, scientists hope the day will come when no earthquake will arrive unheralded. Meanwhile seismologists advocate sea walls and earthquake-proof buildings that could save lives when the restless earth writhes and threatens to wrench apart fragile, man-made structures.

8

Subterranean Secrets

One day several years ago an urgent radio message reached the schooner *Vema,* then in the Strait of Magellan at the southern tip of South America. It requested that the ship's chief scientist, Dr. Maurice Ewing, meet with government officials in Dallas, Texas. They hoped he might be able to suggest techniques for distinguishing between earthquakes and atomic tremors originating on some remote plain or Arctic waste in the U.S.S.R.

Dr. Ewing, despite his experiences in seismic depth sounding, had no ready answer, but he and scientists specializing in seismology were eager to develop a seismometer that could tell the difference between natural quakes and man-made blasts. Quite apart from patriotic reasons, they had an interest in atomic explosions. Artificially induced detonations would give added opportunities for research on the behavior of underground waves.

Seismologists requested that they be alerted ahead of time on A-bomb tests in this country. They could set up special instruments and work out controlled experiments if they had the advantage of knowing exactly where the disturbance originated, and could observe how and where the waves traveled through the earth.

Seismologists participated actively in an underground atomic test in September, 1957, known as Operation Plumb Bob. They learned that an atomic blast gives off a quick, sharp, clean detonation, whereas an earthquake usually starts with slight tremors and builds up. The energy released by an atomic blast is a mere sputter compared with that of a full-fledged quake. It is estimated, for example, that the San Francisco earthquake of 1906 released 100,000 times more energy than the bomb dropped on Hiroshima in 1945. But an underground atomic explosion is more easily recorded than a quake.

Research carried on by seismologists proved to be so helpful that the Defense Department's Advanced Research Projects Agency set up a sixty-six million dollar program known as "Vela" to help seismologists to learn to distinguish between earthquake waves and man-made ones.

Because weak blasts tended to be obscured by the noise of local, ever-present earth quivers called microseisms, Dr. Maurice Ewing devised a highly selective long-wave analyzer to filter these out.

The original project—the observation of atomic bomb blasts for military information—broadened into Operation Plowshare, devoted to peaceful uses of atomic energy underground. This involved members of the engineering geology branch of the United States Geological Survey of Denver, Colorado, as well as seismologists.

Test explosions of TNT were set off below the surface of the same mountain overlooking Yucca Flats where atomic blasts had been tested. The only noticeable surface effects were big clouds of dust and slight tremors of the earth. As a result of a series of blasts, seismologists, geologists and members of the Atomic Energy Commission revealed a number of exciting possibilities for the beneficial use of subterranean nuclear explosions. Artificial canals and harbors could be created quickly and cheaply by this method. If sealed in, the heat generated by an explosion could be retained for years and used to produce power. Controlled atomic blasts might be used to break down the walls of canyons and pitch the material across the bottom, thus creating stable rock-filled dams to hold back flood waters.

Added dividends for the geologists participating in Operation Plowshare were opportunities to study the behavior of seismic waves and magma or molten rock. Both TNT and atomic blasts create magma. In atomic blasts much of the energy released is in the form of heat, which is expended in melting the surrounding rock and vaporizing any water that might be present.

The success of seismologists in using instruments to answer questions about the earth's internal forces led to the application of the same techniques in prospecting for petroleum. Seismic surveying makes use of vibrations or shock waves created artificially by the use of explosives.

A seismologist or oil hunter trained in seismological techniques makes a miniature earthquake by drilling or digging a hole in the ground and detonating a small charge of dynamite. The vibrations are recorded on seismometers or on detectors called geophones, which measure the travel time of the waves from the explosion point to the reflecting area and then back to the surface.

Geophone and seismograph records tell seismologists much about the kind, character and depth of various strata. Vibrations are transmitted, reflected or refracted according to laws governing wave motion. For example, waves are reflected more strongly from very hard rocks than from those compacted from softer material.

If the squiggles on the seismograph are small, it can be assumed that the waves are traveling through a substance such as sandstone which is a good transmitter. When large, heavy lines are recorded, the seismologist knows they indicate a strong, reflecting surface such as limestone, a good source of petroleum. This seismic, or echo-sounding, method of prospecting is widely used where formations in rock strata are sought as an indication of the presence of oil. It eliminates expensive, tedious drilling.

But results may be fuzzy or valueless in regions where limestone is not present or where sediments are poorly consolidated. Seismic prospecting is also expensive because it requires elaborate equipment and teams of trained geophysicists.

Large oil companies find seismic prospecting well worth the expense. Socony Mobile Company employed geologists with an understanding of seismological principles and also trained as frogmen to make surveys in the Gulf of Mexico. By studying echoes and applying their knowledge of seismology to underwater prospecting in much the same way as they had in land tests, they located areas on the ocean floor which seemed to promise oil.

More recently, officials of the Shell Oil Company equipped four vessels for a major long-range seismic search for oil off the California coast. Geologists aboard depend upon standard seismic techniques but they also use a new one called the spark method, whereby an electrical impulse is sent down through the ocean. Echoes from such impulses give an even more detailed picture of geologic structures beneath the floor of the ocean than echoes from explosives.

Seismologists have not only cooperated with atomic scientists and oil tycoons, but have also teamed up with geophysicists in attempting to explain man's world to man. The geophysicists, who by careful calculations fit together data from various fields, but primarily from geology and physics, have been confronted by many puzzling questions as to what lies in the depths below. They want to know whether earth's core is solid or is a hot, seething liquid. They want to know if the earth is a permanent magnet, and how much it is deformed by the pull of the moon and sun.

Drillings, even cores taken at the bottom of the ocean, have penetrated only a few of the four thousand miles which lie between the surface and the center of the earth. Armed with special gravimeters, scientists have fanned out all over the world to measure earth tides—motions in the earth's crust similar to the ebb and flow of the ocean, but much smaller.

Dr. George Woollard, a University of Wisconsin scientist under the sponsorship of Woods Hole Oceanographic Institution, sledged through blizzards and flew through monsoons to take gravity readings in eighty-five countries. Once, before the Chinese Nationalists fled to Formosa, he jeeped through a gap in communist lines to plant meters atop the Shantung mountains in China. Later, Dr. Benioff, using extensometers that measure the strain occurring in rock as a result of tidal pull from the sun and moon, found that the earth bulged and pulsed seven or eight inches at the most.

So far, the wiggly lines of seismograph records have been the earth scientist's best key to the earth's interior. By studying the tremors that constantly run through the earth, whether set off by man-made explosions or earthquakes, seismologists have learned much about structure and composition. Waves flowing out from a shock center are measurable. The way they bend and refract, and their behavior in solids—totally different from their behavior in liquids—give many clues. Dr. Hugo Benioff of the California Institute of Technology developed an especially sensitive seismometer that could detect waves much weaker than ever before recorded.

Through laborious, patient study of the characteristics and travel time of earth waves, seismologists have evolved a fairly good idea of the composition of the earth. They believe it to be divided into three major zones: crust, mantle and core. Their exploration of the outermost layer, the crust, has raised almost as many questions as it has answered because it is such a jumble of materials and physical features. During the International Geophysical Year, scientists investigated one hitherto little known area of the crust, the Antarctic.

Seismic traverse parties plumbed the thickness of the Antarctic ice by bombardment. They could estimate the depth of the ice by the length of time it took seismic waves to return to the seismometric recorders. A hundred miles east of Byrd Station, scientists found ice fourteen thousand feet thick resting on bedrock eight thousand feet below sea level. A study of the Andes substantiated the theory that great mountain bulks "float" in the crustal material that surrounds them, much as an iceberg floats in water.

Geophysicists believe that in most places the crust extends down to a depth of twenty or thirty miles. The upper layers are composed largely of acid, crystalline rocks such as granite with the lower layers mostly basaltic rocks.

Below the earth's crust is the Mohorovicic discontinuity publicized by Moho experiments. It overlies the mantle. Seismologists observing the behavior of vibrations emanating from earthquakes and explosions noted that waves speeded up when entering the mantle. This gave an important clue, because the denser a material is, the faster it transmits vibrational waves.

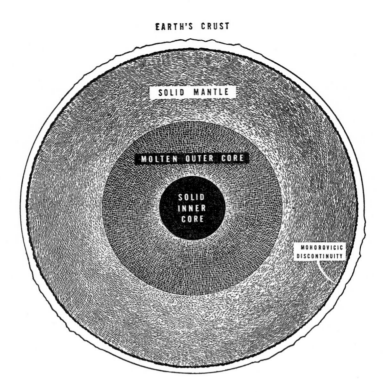

CROSS-SECTION OF THE EARTH (ARTIST'S CONCEPTION)

Seismologists also know that, according to data amassed from observations made in mine shafts and oil wells, the temperature rises with depth—about fifty degrees Fahrenheit per mile of depth. Pressure also increases. Fitting all these bits of information together, seismologists have concluded that rocks beneath the Moho must reach a boiling point, which would result in fusion of rocks and loss of individual identity. This layer of homogenized material, perhaps greenish and gummy, is thought to be about 1,800 miles thick.

There has been much speculation on what constitutes the core. Scientists are agreed that it must be a place of tremendous heat and pressure. Estimates on the pressure run up to twenty-five thousand tons per square inch. Reports of seismologists that S waves were turned back when they reached the core and that P waves

84

decreased sharply led to experiments in the laboratory. Researchers discovered that the action of vibrations moving from silicate materials into iron corresponded with the behavior of P waves entering the core. This substantiated the hunch many seismologists had already arrived at, that the earth has an inner core of red hot nickel or iron. This probability led to the question, Is the iron rigid or in a liquid form?

Dr. Beno Gutenberg, world-famous earthquake expert, directed assistants at the California Tech Laboratory in Pasadena in experiments to determine the effects of pressure and temperature on the rigidity and fluidity of various materials. Harvard scientists worked along the same lines. Trying to duplicate the terrific heat and pressure of the core, they squeezed rocks in gigantic presses and then roasted them in superheated furnaces. Under such treatment, marble and metals flowed like tar. Dr. Gutenberg and others concluded that, because of the great pressures exerted on the inner core, iron could be held rigid even if in liquid form.

The core may hold part of the explanation for the confusing question of earth's magnetism. It is a well-known fact that magnetic poles shift slowly but constantly and that compasses rarely point to the true north. Navigators must always take into account magnetic declination—the difference between geographic north and the direction the compass needle points. In the United States the deviation varies all the way from twenty-two degrees west of north in Maine to twenty-four degrees east of it in Puget Sound.

What causes magnetism has long been a puzzle. Scientists have given answers ranging from the presence of iron to rotation of the earth. Recent studies made by seismologists seem to indicate that electrical currents flowing in the inner core maintain a process similar to that of a self-exciting dynamo. Observations of intensity and direction of magnetic fields will result in better magnetic maps, which in turn will aid navigation. The strength of the earth's magnetism is weaker than was once generally supposed. Sailors in the seventeen hundreds worried that earth's magnetism would pull nails from their boats. Actually, even at the North Pole, the magnetic field is weaker than the pull of a toy horseshoe magnet.

Seismologists and geologists admit freely that they are only at the threshold of understanding the crust, the mantle and the vast, unreachable core. Now they are examining the startling possibility that the earth's crust may be loose and subject to slippage. Crustal shift could, over a long period of time, change the earth's climate and determine the fate of all living things.

Scientists hope in the future to extract more meaning from the wiggly lines of their seismographs. Improved interpretation of readings on their instruments may very well expand our supply of petroleum and other resources, and contribute to intelligent peacetime uses of atomic energy. Seismologists and geophysicists are confident that in the future they will be able to explain that splendid creation, the globe we inhabit, to the men who live upon it.

9

Nature's Spitfires

On January 9, 1960, in the little village of Kapoho on the island of Hawaii, vibrations shook window panes, but the natives went ahead preparing poi and pruning their papaya trees. Meanwhile scientists from the Hawaiian Volcano Observatory, manning a green jeep and a portable seismograph, raced from village streets to cane fields and back again. The jiggly, almost incessant recordings alarmed Dr. Jerry Eaton, stocky young seismologist of the Observatory staff. None of the readings indicated a major quake, but earth tremors and volcanoes are often closely related.

Doctor Eaton telephoned the previously alerted Civil Defense Headquarters in Hilo, twenty-four miles away. "An eruption is almost certain," he warned. "If we're going to get these people out of here, let's do it now."

Civil Defense officials and the Observatory staff supervised the evacuation of the three hundred villagers. Then, watching from a safe vantage point, the natives saw an avalanche of flaming lava pour down the mountainside toward Kapoho. It inundated their orchards and sugar cane fields; it curled around trees and telephone poles that flared up like torches and then fell inert. Days later, disordered chunks of black lava, some to the depth of fifty feet, covered the ground where Kapoho had stood.

Volcanoes are Nature's way of letting off steam. People living in the vicinity of these underground furnaces never know exactly when a fiery mountain will menace their property and their lives.

Volcanists, powerless to prevent eruptions, are dedicated to the ideal of preventing loss of life as a result of such upheavals. Through a study of causes and effects, they determine how the lava flow may be diverted from cities, and how toxic the gases emitted will be. In their quest for the how and why of eruptions, they often travel long distances.

Geologist Haroun Tazieff set up a camp in the Belgian Congo to observe Kituro, a fiery mountain in the process of creation in Africa. One morning he was awakened by what sounded like elephants stampeding. Then he realized Kituro had erupted. He dressed rapidly, seized a camera and instructed his native assistant Paya to follow him with a cinécamera and equipment.

As he emerged from the forest, Tazieff saw spatter cones with red lava flying up out of them. To reach a suitable elevation for taking pictures he climbed a pile of boulders. Sulphurous fumes poured down on him, and the restlessness of the lava seething in the basin below him warned of danger. Still, eager to learn more about the mechanics of eruption, he set up his camera and began filming.

Suddenly the pool of lava swelled up and overflowed. His first reaction was fear of being cut off, but the desire for documentary pictures held him rooted. Then Paya yelled, "Run, Bwana, run!"

With horror Tazieff realized it was too late to run. Ahead lay a molten pool. To the left and to the right flowed streams of red hot lava. Back of him rose a vertical cliff. Ruefully he recalled a cardinal rule among volcanists: Never approach flowing lava without a clear line of retreat. Desperation gave him unusual strength, and he managed to scale the cliff.

Lone observers such as Tazieff share their findings with volcanists on observatory staffs around the world, and they have built up an impressive body of information. But there is still no generally accepted theory on what causes volcanoes to erupt. Obviously it takes a tremendous expulsive energy to drive lava upward out of the network of tubes where it has collected. It is possible that atmospheric conditions affect eruptions, for even a slight change in barometric pressure means that nearly a million tons of weight has been removed from each square mile of the earth's surface.

Some volcanists believe that there is an elastic force within the lava. Others point out that water coming into contact with volcanic heat would be converted into steam with great expansive power. In some eruptions it has been established that gas has accumulated underneath lava hardened from previous eruptions. Beneath the plug, pressure has built up in much the same manner as that produced in soda water in a heated bottle. Eventually the volcano blows its top. Earthquakes sometimes goad volcanoes into action. As a result of the earthquake in Peru in 1960, six old volcanoes cracked open and three new ones came to angry life.

Volcanists spend more time studying the effects of volcanoes than the causes, for unless they know how a volcano will behave, they cannot give sound advice on protective measures. No two volcanoes ever perform in exactly the same way.

Some volcanoes, like Stromboli, the "lighthouse of the Mediterranean," are perpetually active. Others, like Lassen Peak in Lassen Volcanic National Park, show signs of life only spasmodically. In May of 1914 Lassen ejected dust and steam. Three years later, lava spilled over the rim. Although temporarily out of business, Lassen could erupt again, but the once-active volcanoes Shasta, Hood and Rainier give no signs of future activity. Eruptions frequently cause widespread havoc. But Etna, despite its thundering voice, pitchy clouds and fiery lava, usually stops short of death-dealing destruction.

Hawaiian-type volcanoes pour forth massive quantities of lava, but normally there is no smoke, no fire and no spectacular explosion. What appears to be smoke is actually steam mixed with dust and gases, and what looks like fire is the reflection of glowing, white-hot lava on the clouds above. The proportion of gas is small compared with the amount of lava.

Volcanoes classified as Vesuvian and deriving their name from the famous volcano of Vesuvius on the Bay of Naples, are characterized by spells of violent activity with tremendous explosions accompanied by ash, slag, and colossal dark clouds of gas and steam, but very little lava.

CINDER CONE

SHIELD CONE

TWO TYPES OF VOLCANO CONES

Even the lava spilled forth by volcanoes differs in quality. One type of lava, Aa, is rough and often glows as it creeps forward in menacing fury. Paehoe, more like a sticky, molten porridge, flows with quiet ease.

Whenever possible, volcanists get samples of lava at the time of an eruption so they can subject it to various tests which may reveal answers on effects and also on formation. After the Kilauea Iki

90

eruption in Hawaii in 1959, geochemist Wayne Ault of the Hawaiian Volcano Observatory Staff donned Fiberglas coveralls so he could approach the golden torrent of hot lava. With tongs he succeeded in pinching up samples of lava, but the lack of ventilation in his fireproof suit left him soaked with perspiration. "The suit repelled heat all right," he reported to his colleagues, "but it was like wearing a portable oven."

Volcanists working near the fountain of lava wore hard hats and masks as protection against choking fumes and the brick-sized chunks of pumice flying through the air. When a thick crust formed on top of the lava lake, Observatory scientists walked across it to observe splatter cones, although one misstep could have plunged them into annihilation. To a reporter who questioned him on the safety of the activity, Dr. Jerry Eaton, then Director of the Volcano Observatory, said, "When we take chances we also take precautions." But spectators wondered what the precautions were.

The discharge of gases which often accompanies eruptions is another dangerous variable. At Martinique, in the West Indies, most of the twenty-six thousand victims of an eruption perished from inhalation of fumes rather than from inundation by lava. Even after an eruption has spent itself, the carbon dioxide bubbling up may be sufficient to kill birds or mice. In Death Valley, Java, larger animals such as the tiger or rhinoceros often die from exposure to volcanic gas.

To collect gas samples for their experimentation, geochemists equipped with pumps and vacuum tubes clamber up and down the steep sides of craters of extinct volcanoes. After the explosion of Kilauea Iki, Wayne Ault wheedled the pilot of a National Guard plane into flying low over the crater. By holding test tubes out of the window, he captured gases, but the fumes of sulphur dioxide made him ill.

Painstaking laboratory studies on samples from numerous volcanoes have proved that gases of the hydrogen, carbon, sulphur and nitrogen group are present in many eruptions. Most of these are very explosive and some are poisonous. Evil-smelling hydrogen sulphide may sicken or even prove fatal to its victims.

91

In addition to analyzing samples of lava and gas, volcanists at the time of an eruption note carefully the number of explosions, maximal intensity and sequence of incidents. Because photographs can be studied later and compared with those of previous eruptions or from other lands, volcanists try to take pictures at close range. They also look for signs of atmospheric disturbances and changes in topography.

Following the death-dealing 1883 eruption of Krakatoa, in a strait between Java and Sumatra, clouds of volcanic dust so darkened the sun that natives of Batavia a hundred miles away had to light their lamps. Elsewhere sunsets had unaccustomed beauty because the volcanic dust provided nuclei around which moisture could condense. Wind-borne around the globe, it blanketed the sun and caused unusually cold weather all over the world.

It is not at all unusual for islands to be formed by volcanic eruption. Ascension, the only dry bit of land between the hump of Brazil and the bulge of Africa, is an example. Sometimes volcanoes thrust up whole mountains: the Spanish Peaks in southeastern Colorado are actually cones formed of basalt, a dark, heavy lava rich in iron. Other eruptions leave yawning craters in which, if the volcano becomes extinct, lakes may form. Crater Lake in Oregon is six miles long and two thousand feet deep.

Between eruptions, scientists study the characteristics of volcanoes that are resting, for they are, in a sense, windows to the earth's interior. Volcanists measure temperatures in craters or lava lakes with pyrometers built to withstand extreme heat. As they analyze the magma and gases, they constantly seek more knowledge of the origin of volcanic heat and what subterranean mechanisms trigger a volcano. The biggest net gain of such studies has been increased efficiency in forecasting eruptions.

While serving as head of the Hawaiian Volcano Observatory, Dr. Jaggar came to the conclusion that volcanic eruptions, at least in that area, had a periodicity in occurrence. He also suspected that before an eruption there might be telltale signs in temperature or in activity of lava. Over a period of weeks he and his assistants made round-the-clock observations of Halemaumau, the lava lake in the floor of Kilauea. The data they acquired convinced Dr. Jaggar that the lake had a daily tide resulting both from solar and lunar effects, but before an eruption the tide rose, pushing lava up in bulges.

Today, tilt-meters, designed to measure by leveling, register the upthrusts in lava which are considered danger signals. Because tilt-meters operate more accurately in darkness than in daylight, staff members of the Hawaiian Volcano Observatory make their rounds of the intricate network each night—even on cold, rainy ones. That is only one aspect of the tedious, hard work and dedication to duty involved in their kind of forecasting.

There is sometimes risk too. In the Dutch East Indies, daring volcanists patrol the side of a threatening volcanic cone. An absolutely hermetic underground shelter, equipped with oxygen cylinders, enables observers to remain there even in case of an eruption.

Patrols and instruments aid volcanists in their forecasts but do not completely eliminate guesswork. In 1959 scientists expected a flow of lava from Kilauea; but the lava, when it came, flowed from the subsidiary crater Iki. At such times volcanists feel that their research is as inadequate as were the appeasing actions of natives in Hawaii of long ago who threw carcasses of pigs into the craters in the hope of propitiating Pele, the ill-tempered goddess of volcanoes. However, in a number of instances volcanists have predicted accurately the time, type, direction of flow and degree of violence of an eruption.

Volcanists tend to adopt the attitude that they don't really make predictions but report conditions and try to interpret what they mean. Only by continuous records and observations over a long period of years can significant advances be made.

Because volcanoes are many and observatories few, warnings are not always possible. Occasionally a volcano long quiescent and not under observation comes suddenly to life. In October, 1961, on the island of Tristan da Cunha in the South Atlantic, a volcano which had remained dormant for centuries suddenly erupted. Over two hundred refugees fled aboard fishing vessels to bleak, uninhabited Nightingale Island, thirteen miles away. Stunned and terrified, they huddled together watching the 7,640-foot-high mountain which covered most of their island spout fiery lava that buried their homes.

Occasionally a warning is impossible because a new volcano is born unexpectedly in a remote place. Such was the case in a valley two hundred miles west of Mexico City where, for several days, farmer Dionisio Polido had been puzzled and frightened by wisps of smoke arising from cracks in the ground of his cornfield.

On the morning of February 20, 1943, while the farmer and his oxen rested, Polido felt the earth tremble and heard an angry roar. Ahead of him a monstrous column of smoke boiled into the air and his heaving cornfield emitted fire, sand and ashes. For Polido, who had no interest in owning a volcano instead of a cornfield—and for farmers and the villagers of nearby Paricutin who lost their homes, crops, and cattle when the lava flood came—the eruption spelled disaster. But it gave volcanists the unparalleled opportunity to study a volcano in its early stages.

"Many learned people come here to study the volcano," one peasant complained, "but with all their knowledge not one of them can tell when the volcano is going to be quiet." The volcanic activity continued into the middle of the summer.

As a science, volcanology is still in its infancy and volcanists would be the first to admit its limitations. But a carefully watched volcano can no longer take a populace by surprise.

After Dr. Jaggar's prophecy that Mauna Loa would erupt in 1935, scientists from the Observatory, engineers and civic and military officials drew up plans for a barrier to protect the city of Hilo, and its airport and harbor facilities, which Dr. Jaggar predicted would be threatened. The Red Cross, National Guard and American Legion were alerted to come to the rescue if evacuation became a necessity.

On December 25, a river of lava threatened Hilo's water supply and the city itself. Dr. Jaggar outlined a plan, previously discussed with the General Hawaiian Department of Defense, for diverting the lava away from Hilo. The surface of lava, he explained, had solidified; but underneath, molten lava flowed ceaselessly forward.

Bombing from the air, if done precisely, might demolish the roof, dam the liquid lava with debris, and force it to overflow in a direction where it would cause less harm. Flying above the river of lava with military personnel, Dr. Jaggar indicated target areas.

All day long on December 27 the planes moaned overhead at twenty-minute intervals, dropping bombs that detonated noisily. By noon on December 28 direct hits had blasted off the hardened surface. Some of the lava had been dammed, the rest of it gave evidence of cooling and solidifying.

Some who objected to the expense of the bombing insisted that the lava stream would have died out with no interference. The bombing, they contended, had been no more effective than the antics of a princess who in 1881 supposedly stopped a Mauna Loa flow by cutting off some of her hair and tossing it into the advancing lava while intoning mystical formulas. But most persons, convinced that the bombing had saved millions of dollars worth of property, commended the procedure.

Through self-discipline, courage and conscientious effort, volcanists have taken the painful steps that have brought them closer not only to an understanding of volcanoes but to the earth that spews them forth. Geologists may initially be attracted to a study of volcanoes by a great sense of wonder, a taste for danger and an attraction for the unknown. But it is the knowledge that their work can benefit humanity, that there is a solution, and that the solution is worth the seeking that keeps them plodding through innumerable laboratory tests, compiling statistics, enduring fumes, and descending into fiery craters.

In Hawaii, volcanists have made great strides in convincing the public that although volcanic eruptions cannot be prevented, people can avoid submitting to their effects. However, in many places, the measures taken are inadequate for full protection. Volcanists dream of the day when there will be observatories in every area menaced by active volcanoes. Adequate warning systems and protective measures could prevent any city from being engulfed by a flaming flood of lava as was the little village of Kapoho.

10

Spouters and Springs

Indians and trappers alike once feared the Yellowstone region. Evil-smelling sulphur fumes that looked like smoke, as well as the seared skeleton-trees, suggested an entrance to the infernal regions. The hollow drumming of horses' hoofs upon the white, crusty earth indicated that caverns lay beneath. It was no wonder that scouts and trappers gave such names to the region as Brimstone Basin and Hell's Half Acre.

Geological information banished superstition and tall tales about the spouters but did not completely answer such questions as: Why does some of the water remain in hot springs instead of gushing up volumes of water and steam as geysers do? What is the mechanism of geysers? How can their heat and power be made to serve mankind?

To find answers, geologists at geyser basins in Yellowstone Park, New Zealand and Iceland make extensive drill holes, lower thermometers into springs and study the geological formations that lie exposed on canyon walls. They analyze samples of rock brought up from the underground and the white sinter overlying many of the basins.

Geysers differ widely in character, appearance and performance. Some hot-water geysers have pools that vary from a deep vivid blue with remarkable transparency to masses of seething mud. The Yellowstone Paint Pot area, a multicolored cauldron formed by subterranean streams, tosses mud clots into the air. Pink, blue, or cream-colored, they frequently spread out in the shape of flowers.

Many geysers have cones formed when overflowing water cooled and deposited minerals in mounds which range in shape from bee-hives to castles. The sinter surrounding many of the geysers is composed mostly of silica deposited by evaporation of water.

Geysers differ in the height and frequency of their eruptions. Old Faithful, after a few uncertain puffs, blasts forth a great tower of hot water and hissing steam which rises hundreds of feet into the air. Some small geysers listlessly lift a tiny column of water. Old Faithful has a regular cycle of eruption, coming to life almost hourly, but others perform at unpredictable intervals. Some geysers overflow continually.

That soap stimulates geyser activity was discovered by accident. A man of Chinese extraction who worked in the Park regularly washed his clothes in the hot water provided by nature. One day when he accidentally dropped a bar of soap into the spring, the chemical reaction blasted the laundryman's clothes forty feet into the air. From that day the spring was known as Chinaman's Spring.

Geologists and other scientists interested in geo-energetics (the study of what goes on far below the surface of the earth) have concentrated on the hidden aspects of geysers. Only through understanding the origin and mechanics of underground heat and power could scientists determine of what use these might be to humanity. Their findings show that to exist, geysers must have water, heat and a plumbing system that will withstand high pressures. The source of water for geysers is the moisture that seeps into the ground as the result of rainfall. If this water lies over a volcano which has been active in the past, gases arising from below prevent its sinking to any great depth. As the water absorbs gases, it becomes an active solvent and forms larger cavities. This gas-impregnated water in storage and under pressure is the first requisite of a geyser.

Active or extinct volcanoes supply the second ingredient—heat. Carbon dioxide, sulphureted hydrogen and minor quantities of other gases rise from deep-seated hot rocks which originally supplied volcanic lava. Under Yellowstone Park these rocks are very hot:

a thermometer lowered into a hole drilled to the depth of four hundred and six feet in the Upper Geyser Basin showed a temperature of three hundred and sixty degrees. Hot gases moving upward under pressure heat the lower layer of the underground water. Eventually the water boils and produces steam bubbles which rise, aerate, and boost the temperature of the column of water above.

As the process continues, the steam increases and seeks an outlet in Nature's plumbing—an intricate network of underground channels, fissures and passageways. The decrease of pressure caused by the steam's escaping into whatever outlets it can find permits a new influx of steam and gas from below. Eventually, imprisoned water expanding into still more steam builds up energy enough to lift whatever water may be above it and toss it into the air.

Yellowstone geysers squirt scalding water, but occasionally in mining areas cold-water geysers develop as the result of drilling for oil. Trapped carbon dioxide carbonizes the water, which then begins to ascend the drill hole. Release of pressure further activates the dissolved gas and speeds an eruption.

Geysers are in all stages of development, and their underground mechanism constantly changes. More often than not, changes are gradual, but occasionally they may be sudden and violent. The 1959 earthquake in Yellowstone caused some totally new geysers to burst forth, but Turquoise Pool, long a beautiful landmark, deteriorated into a mudhole. Sometimes silica clogging underground water passages causes a geyser to cease functioning.

For years geologists could not explain why some of the water in Yellowstone gushed up in geysers, while at other places it lay in a placid pool or flowed gently over terraces as at Mammoth Hot Springs. Geologists now believe that, particularly in a sandy area, the violent action of a geyser may destroy the underground plumbing. Then the water rises to the surface as a hot spring. But if water entering a geyser basin encounters obstacles and has to travel in a roundabout way, pressure develops. The water reaching the surface only intermittently explodes into a geyser.

Another change likely to occur is the evolution of fumaroles into geysers. Both are associated with volcanic areas, but fumaroles eject only steam. The most spectacular recent appearance of fumaroles was in Alaska where a volcanic eruption wrenched open hundreds of vents in the surface of the ground. Later, when steam poured forth dramatically, the area was christened the Valley of Ten Thousand Smokes. When the valley cools enough for vents near the surface to retain water, the steam jets will become geysers.

Biologists as well as geologists have an interest in geysers because of the effects of underground heat on plants and animals. Observations have been made in Yellowstone Park both in summer and winter. Plant and animal life flourish beyond the range of the geysers and their pools, but close to the gushers, because of the extreme heat and the poor quality of the soil, mostly sinter, life is limited to algae. These tiny plants made of myriads of small filaments lend color to the pools, and there is one bright yellow species that can withstand temperatures hot enough to kill insects.

Geysers are less hostile to animals in winter than in summer. Despite subzero weather, geyser water maintains temperatures up to a hundred and ninety degrees and the area surrounding the spouter remains snow-free. Sea gulls and pelicans snatch up bits of food, and elk graze along the banks of warm streams and the meadows in front of Old Faithful Inn. Attracted by the welcome warmth, park animals boldly approach the geysers. A few times large animals have met death when the thin crust gave way and they toppled into scalding water.

Geysers provide laboratories for meteorologists. Dr. Vincent Schaefer, innovator in the modern cloud-seeding techniques, conceived the idea that Yellowstone would afford excellent opportunities for experimentation on atmospheric conditions, since the collision of warm and cold air masses determines weather; so in the winter of 1960–61 he headed an eight-man testing expedition to that area, under the auspices of the Atmospheric Research Center of the State University of New York and the National Science Foundation. The scientists had the assistance of the National Park Service and Forest Service officials. During the eight days Dr. Schaefer and his co-workers spent in the Park, the weather was unusually mild. This fact interfered with seeding of the steam clouds with silver iodide, because this chemical requires below-freezing temperatures to be effective. However, Dr. Schaefer introduced carbon dioxide into the steam and succeeded in producing a cloud of crystals that increased natural concentration by about a million times. The expedition concluded that geysers could provide further valuable data in the future.

Icelanders have put their underground sources of heat and power to an even more practical use than atmospheric research. Although thirteen per cent of Iceland lies rigid beneath a permanent cover of ice and snow, its thermal activity is intense. Hot springs, fumaroles and geysers abound.

When country women in large numbers flocked to the hot springs to do their laundry, Icelanders began asking why they couldn't use this lavish bounty of nature more effectively. Geothermal experts agreed that it would indeed be possible to utilize the supply of free heat.

For a pilot project, scientists selected a field some miles east of the capital city, Reykjavik, where small geysers gushed and springs gurgled up out of the ground. Engineers, relying on scientific data, drilled down to good sources of heat and then pumped it into pipes leading to storage tanks. Because of the cold climate, the water had a lower temperature than that in Yellowstone and had to be pumped quickly to avoid loss of heat. From storage tanks the hot water descended by gravity into the city, where it circulated in pipes and radiators of homes, schools, and other public buildings. Wonderfully soft, the water flowed from taps at temperatures between seventy-five and eighty degrees.

The first heating plant was crude, but its success led to the erection of a fine, modern one. This plant does not supply warmth for all of Reykjavik, but where the naturally heated water is used no furnace is needed and the city remains unsullied by smoke. Not far below the Arctic Circle, greenhouse owners, using the new type of heat, grow vegetables and tropical bananas.

Scientists exploring the field of geo-energetics were convinced that geysers, springs, and fumaroles could also be made to provide power. At Lardarello, near Florence, Italy, a plant was established

101

using geothermal energy supplied by fumaroles. Turbines propelled by underground steam supplied electricity to several cities.

Engineers of the Pacific Gas and Electric Company relied on findings from geo-energetic studies when they built in California the first steam-geyser electric plant in the Western Hemisphere. The noisy, high-pressure formations located between Geyserville and Calistoga—popularly known as geysers but really fumaroles—had previously been only a scenic attraction. Now they generated power. A pipeline carried the captured steam from capped geysers that emitted strident screams to generators which converted it into power at about a third of the cost of conventional methods.

New Zealand, confronted with an acute need for power, turned to subterranean heat utilizing both natural fumaroles and man-made boreholes. In the Wairakei thermal region gigantic plumes of silvery steam hover over a complicated system of subterranean pipelines. Steam piped to the surface from this "hot spot" powers turbines and generates the electricity that New Zealanders use to toast bread, run vacuum cleaners and illuminate their homes.

In some parts of the Wairakei region, geothermal bores are delivering more steam today than when originally drilled. At present the supply of steam appears to be inexhaustible.

Geothermal experts are gratified that their findings have helped in the solution of problems in Iceland and New Zealand, but alongside the solutions are haunting unknowns. The geological conditions which produce geothermal areas are still not fully understood. It is possible that other formations aside from the kind found at Lardarello and Wairakei are just as useful sources of steam but are being bypassed through ignorance. There is a need for a worldwide survey of potential geothermal areas.

As yet no accurate method has been developed for assessing the productivity and lifetime of a borehole. Research, experimentation and pilot projects will have to be undertaken to determine whether the new sources of heat and energy—geysers, hot springs and fumaroles—will be usable on a really large scale.

Meanwhile, operating on the philosophy that steam, like gold, is where you find it, scientists doing research in geo-energetics have

102

been discovering sources of steam where surface indications are completely absent. There are also many fumaroles and hot springs as yet undeveloped—some of them in nations greatly in need of power.

That same geological know-how that has learned the mechanisms of geysers, springs and fumaroles will devise new ways to use their heat and power. Already the underground forces once considered fearsome have been harnessed to help heat homes and factories and keep turbines turning.

11

Conundrums in Caves

How are caves formed, and how do dwellers in the dark differ from fish, animals and insects living outside? Could caves provide suitable shelter in military emergencies, and are they too humid to be used for storing art treasures and microfilm records? To answer such questions as these, geologists, naturalists, nuclear physicists, biologists, and speleologists lower themselves into sunless abysses, squirm through s-holes, and feel their way along underground precipices.

One of the main objects of the biologists is to discover how animals and plants adapt to perpetual darkness. Plants are limited to those that can draw nourishment from the air, from minerals or from decaying organisms. One kind of moss thrives in dark crevices, but it is hard to detect because it resembles the rocks around it. In some tropical caves, trees grow from cocorite palm seeds dropped by oilbirds or fruit eating bats, but these are stunted and soon collapse.

Animal life in caves is more abundant and includes such unique creatures as transparent shrimp and blind salamanders. Caves usually have three zones, each with its own population. The area just inside the entrance is a shelter area, where animals enter briefly for a nap or temporary protection from a storm. Silver-flecked Arkansas salamanders retreat there during hot weather. Cave rats, pilferers and hoarders, whether on the inside or outside, store their treasures of tinfoil and trinkets in this entrance zone or in the twilight zone beyond, where they may have the companionship of weasels. Some animals and insects spend most of their time in the twilight zone but are equally at home in other moist, dark situations beneath logs or rocks. Rodents and cave crickets venture forth at night.

But the cave dwellers that most interest biologists are those that live permanently in the darkest interior. What structural adaptations permit these animals to adjust to caves? Can they provide us a link with the past? Denizens of the darkness are usually small, often colorless, and can easily hide in cracks. Finding them is often a slow, painful process involving crawling narrow passageways, crossing underground lakes and slithering along muddy slopes.

For purposes of collecting and recording his finds, the biologist or ichthyologist needs special equipment. He must also tote the standard gear used by speleologists: ropes, pitons, hard hats and three sources of light—a head lamp, flashlight, Coleman lantern or candles and a package of waterproof matches.

Even when scientists follow all the rules set down by the National Speleological Society for safe cave exploring, unforeseen occurrences may menace their lives. Scientists Kenneth N. Dearolf and Charles E. Mohr, later director of the Audubon Nature Center at Greenwich, Connecticut, once went to Moore's cave near Springfield, Arkansas, where they hoped to find blind fish. This cave, located in a pasture, had a narrow, steep chimney opening. Squirming down a crawlway to a ledge, the two explorers found a small stream that flowed past them and then formed a waterfall that plunged to a room below.

Mohr wanted to descend to the chamber beneath them. Dearolf hesitated, pointing out that they had only a light, fifty-foot rope and no safety rope, but Mohr argued that the drop was only a short one. After securing the rope over a projecting rock at the side of the waterfall, he started down. But the rope had nothing to hold it taut, and about halfway down Mohr swung under the waterfall. The increase in weight when the water poured into his hip boots made him loose his grip. He landed on the rocks below. He was winded, soaked, and momentarily blind because his glasses had

106

been knocked off, but the fall had only bruised him. Recovering his flashlight and his glasses, still intact, he decided that while he was down he might as well do some research.

"Send my collecting kit down," he called to Dearolf.

Dearolf lowered the kit. Splashing around in a knee-deep pool, Mohr caught two pure white crayfish; then he saw a tiny, pearl-white fish he thought to be a blind fish. He made a swift pass at it with his hands, but the fish disappeared. Mohr stood motionless, hoping that it would swim back. While he waited, he heard a roar. Suddenly the ceiling of the room seemed lower. With a sinking heart he realized that the water must be rushing in from the outside. The room would soon be flooded. He ran to grasp the end of the rope, but it didn't reach far enough down. "Get help from the nearest farm," he shouted to Dearolf.

To save the batteries in his flashlight, Mohr turned out the light. Minutes dragged by. Water mounted to his waist. Trying to overcome the violent chills that had beset him he flailed his body with his arms.

Finally a sturdy rope snaked down, but Mohr had nothing to brace himself against and the water pouring down upon him battered him unmercifully. Gasping for breath, half paralyzed by cold, he struggled up the rope hand over hand. Halfway up he saw a ledge. Kicking against it and then using the rope as a pendulum, he swung in a wider arc until he got a footing on the shelf. There he rested a few moments. Then he climbed upward once more until Dearolf could pull him from the torrent.

"That's what caused the trouble," said Dearolf as Mohr staggered from the cave. He nodded toward the raging torrent created by a cloudburst. When Mohr and Dearolf had entered the cave it had been but a trickle.

Despite his rugged experience, Mohr was determined to have another look at the elusive fish. Three weeks later he and Dearolf returned to the cave. This time they had better equipment. While Mohr was trying to capture the fish, he found that it seemed sensitive to vibrations. The ability of the fish to detect a slight disturbance in the water, he found out later, was due to papillae, each tipped with sensitive nerve endings, arranged in rows over the top and sides of the fish's head and jaws. Prominent eyelike structures were really masses of fatty tissue in which were buried minute, atrophied eyes.

Cave-dwelling salamanders, as well as fishes, have lost their power to see. The absence of light in caves makes sight of little use to its inhabitants. To compensate for their loss of sight, cave animals have overdeveloped organs of touch. The feelers of cave crickets are about three times the length of their bodies. Blind animals also have a supersensitive sense of smell and hearing.

Biologists have learned that because the humidity and temperature of their environment remain almost constant, cave animals do not need furry coats as a protection against the cold. Nor is pigmentation essential where there is no light. Most cave dwellers are pale or a spooky white in color. Some shrimp are so transparent that they can best be recognized by the shadow they cast when a flashlight surprises them. Research carried out by biologists reveals that these animals living deep in caves must depend for food on bacteria, insects transported by bats, or on fungus spores wafted in by air drafts. Some material is carried in by rain freshets or waters of rivers that leave their surface channels to travel underground. But at best the diet of cave animals is meager, and the limited food supply keeps them tiny and spindly. Many cave animals are so small that they can easily be mistaken for a bit of gravel.

Biologists often find daddy longlegs, scorpions, spiders and beetles in caves. There are also flatworms that twist and turn in odd shapes. Perhaps the strangest inhabitants of caves are the Stars of Death, natives of New Zealand. This worm, with a pale gray transparent skin and a body no longer than a pin, is a grub stage of fly. Its numerous sticky threads trap moths and gnats. In Waitomo Caves myriads of these worms hang from the ceiling. Guides lead sightseers into a vaulted chamber and then turn off all man-made light. Because these worms have a segment that gleams with a light like that of a firefly, the ceiling glows with blue-green stars.

Only infrequently are birds found in caves. The only true avian dweller is the guacháro, or oilbird, of Venezuela.

108

Concentrations of bats in caves have given biologists the opportunity for intensive studies. Although the flying mammals are not blind, they see poorly in daytime. To avoid collisions when in flight they make sounds inaudible to human ears. Bouncing back when they hit a solid body, the sounds warn the bat when to swerve. Although bats migrate, experiments with banded ones show that they tend to return to the same caves year after year. When autumn comes they go into hibernation, hanging downward from cave ceilings, and become so sluggish that if disturbed they merely utter a drowsy protest. However, if roughly handled in warm weather they can use their tiny, sharp teeth with telling effect.

In 1946, throughout areas of Mexico close to the Texas border, many cattle were dying of paralytic rabies and vampire bats were thought to be the carriers. Although these bats are not native to Texas and are not believed to migrate, they can transmit rabies to other bats that do. Texas ranchers feared that the disease would spread to their herds, and Charles E. Mohr, assisted by members of the National Speleological Society, undertook a study of the locale and range of Mexican bats. Working under hazardous conditions, they caught bats and kept them in collecting boxes for observation. Mohr did find infected ones, but the nearest vampire hideout was two hundred and fifty miles south of the Texas border, so Mohr assured ranchers that their herds were safe at least for the time being.

Biologists have been more successful in analyzing habits of animals than in locating those providing links to the past, but tiny blue-gray perchlike fish in Devil's Hole Cave in Nevada indicate an ancient ancestry. Identified as springfish, they are believed to be descendents of fish that once lived in a chain of lakes in the Mojave Desert area. When the lakes drained or evaporated away, only a few pools of water survived.

Geologists as well as biologists enter caves in large numbers seeking answers on the origins and structure of the earth, but frequently their inquiries seek specific information for the use of government or industry.

In February, 1954, the National Speleological Society invited a

109

geological team to go along to make a detailed survey in Crystal Cave, Kentucky, which lies under an island of private property surrounded by Mammoth Cave National Park. Interest in the cave had run high ever since its discoverer, Floyd Collins, had been trapped while exploring a little-known passageway. Rescuers had found a way of feeding Collins, but could not free him; and he had died in the cave he alone had explored. Now the National Speleological Society wanted a report on the structure and resources of Crystal Cave. Equipped with everything from compasses and collecting tools to telephone apparatus and camping equipment, the party of sixty-four amateurs and scientists modeled their expedition on an army field operation. Half the group worked above ground on details of supply.

Because they could assess the safety of an area by examining its structure, geologists were always in the vanguard. In their notebooks they jotted down descriptions of rocks—their appearance and size, and details of bedding, fractures and crystal formations. Occasionally they chipped off samples of rock to be analyzed later. They gathered or made molds of fossils found, and recorded the location of minerals, as well as the direction, velocity and flow of underground streams. Governed by strict discipline and precise timing, the explorers moved along complex passages that branched out like giant spider webs. The unfamiliar darkness, pierced only by pinpoints of light from head lamps or electric torches, gave a sense of unreality to the venture.

Deep in the cave system, the party encountered slippery rocks, canyons and crawlways. Sometimes they had to walk along ledges only inches wide, below which gaped yawning pits. Food supplies and equipment had to be dragged, pushed, lowered, and hoisted. At intervals geologists would call a halt to examine stalactites formed when water percolating through the limestone had become heavily charged with dissolved carbonate of lime and carbon dioxide.

Once panic assailed the explorers when, despite the use of compasses and maps, they could not tell exactly where they were in relation to the maze of passageways. But in the end everyone emerged safely from the cave. Geologists spent days unscrambling notes, analyzing specimens and making a detailed report on their findings. One part of their summation included details on how the cave had been formed.

Crystal Cave, like Carlsbad and most of the other more than five thousand known caves of the United States, is limestone, formed partly from mineral matter, partly from the shells and bones of marine animals that once inhabited inland seas. The minerals dissolved and then gradually cemented into porous masses of limestone. When the seas receded, the limestone remained stranded on dry ground. Through the years, cracks formed and later became channels for streams which ate away the soluble lime. As the water levels fell, underground rivers burrowed deeper, leaving caverns behind.

In many such caves there are flowstone formations, formed by mineral-bearing water streaming rapidly from a crack. Flowstone often develops into graceful curtains of draperies that can seal off portions of a cave into separate rooms. Wind blowing upon the flowing solution sometimes causes it to harden into rippling cascades known as flowing Niagaras.

Geologists have concluded that there are five main classes of caves: limestone, lava, wind, sea and ice. Ice caves form wherever there are glaciers. As a mammoth tongue of glacial ice slides along a canyon, the friction and external warmth cause enough melting to form a stream which hollows out a tunnel. Summer breezes enlarge it. Although glacial caves usually remain very small, Paradise Ice Cave in Stevens Glacier on Mt. Rainier is roomy. A bluish light penetrates the ice.

In total contrast, the great lava caves in the Cascade Range mirror in their walls the blazing heat to which they owe their existence. Geologists have accumulated evidence to prove that along the whole length of the Cascades great volcanoes once spouted lava rivers. As they rolled along, their top layer cooled and hardened into a crust; but the molten mass underneath flowed onward, leaving a hollow tube behind. In most cases these tubes sealed at both ends before the volcano became dormant, but later, worn by the elements, they collapsed.

111

EXPLORING ICE CAVE

Lava tubes are likely to be dull and dreary, but in the Lava Beds National Monument in California some caves are lined with glassy red or green. Silver and Golden Dome cave take their names from the sheen of their ceilings. Crystal Cave has sparkling ice so clear that even rocks two feet behind it are clearly visible.

How ice could form in a volcanic cave baffled geologists for a time. The explanation now offered is depth. Neither earth nor rock is a good conductor of heat. In summer, warm air rises from the entrance and is replaced by cool air drawn through crevices, so the ice never melts.

Sea caves, formed by breakers hammering away at coastal cliffs, are often inaccessible except at low tide. Ordinarily they are less extensive than land caves and lack variety in formations.

Sometimes wind, over a long period of time, wears deep hollows in soft spots in rocks and eventually forms a cave. Wind Cave in the Black Hills was discovered by pioneer Tom Bingham on a hunting trip. Mystified by a whistling sound that seemed to come up out of the ground, he traced it to its source—a ten-inch aperture. When he leaned over to examine it, wind blew his hat up in the air. Bingham rushed off to get a shovel to enlarge the hole. His brother accompanied him back to the site, and their excavation revealed a magnificent cave honeycombed with calcite formations.

While studying the why and how of cave formations, geologists are always on the lookout for materials of economic value. Some caves are sources of onyx. Guano, deposited by bats, is rich in nitrogen and readily saleable as fertilizer. Flawless, transparent calcite can be used in optical instruments, especially certain types of microscopes.

War threats have accelerated interest in underground hideaways for storage depots, shelters, command posts and communications centers. Nuclear physicists have joined the ranks of geologists, biologists and naturalists who have governmental assignments to map and measure caves, and test their humidity and depth of overlay. According to nuclear physicists, there is no more reliable defense against radioactive rays than a cavern in the heart of a mountain, but the cave should have a fifty-foot overlay of rock. If food, fissionable materials or weapons are to be stored, it is important that the cave be relatively dry.

One problem, that of underground communications from cave to cave, is already on the way to solution, through a new method named "Lithcom," which can transmit radio waves along deep-lying strata formations with suitable electrical properties. In July, 1960, a group of electronics engineers of D.E.C.O., Developmental Engineering Corporation, from a cave near Carlsbad, New Mexico, sent a message through the earth to engineers waiting in a distant mine. The waves from a two-hundred watt transmitter traveled at a depth of a thousand feet for four and a half miles. This system, if perfected, would be proof against man-made electrical noise and deliberate jamming.

The use of caves for military production and civilian defense is not new. In World War II almost every nation had some kind of underground facilities. Germany, on the verge of defeat, had almost finished a gigantic jet plane factory under a pine forest near Munich. Sweden found underground centers so effective that burrows for industrial use were blasted out after the war.

Industries essential to defense in the United States may follow Sweden's example. Even less essential industry, plagued by lack of space and high maintenance costs, may move to caves. Underground establishments require no exterior painting or upkeep, and fuel savings are considerable because of the deep interior's constant temperature of from fifty to sixty degrees. In handling certain delicate tools, the lack of vibrations from outside would be a prime advantage. There is also agitation for underground storage of historic documents, microfilm records and art treasures. When requests for surveys of caves for industrial and defense purposes swamped geologists in some areas, speleologists volunteered their services.

Scientists are gradually cracking the conundrums that caves have posed, but plenty of challenges remain for both mind and muscle. Miles of caves yet unexplored extend from Kentucky where the earth is so perforated that it resembles a block of Swiss cheese, under the Ohio River into Indiana and Illinois and under the Mississippi River into Missouri and Arkansas. Some, although explored, have not been surveyed scientifically.

Biologists hope to establish biospeleological laboratories such as the one in the Pyrenees region of France that includes an aquarium and a terrarium (a reservoir for cave-dwelling animals). Geologists will never be content until the space, minerals, water, and other resources of caves have not only been appraised but utilized. They know, also, that in the hollowed-out places of the earth there are undiscovered answers to the how and why of our universe.

114

12

Underground Riches

While studying the possibilities for mining iron ore from the Nimba Mountain Range in Liberia, geologists lived under primitive conditions in corrugated iron shacks. Large black ants that destroyed everything in their path moved into the camp by the million. At this moment mining engineers and geologists are slashing paths in jungles, scaling mountains, slogging through crocodile- and snake-infested swamps in a quest for metals, minerals and oil locked beneath the ground.

Raw materials are the lifeblood of industrialized nations, but as our population has increased, our supplies of copper, iron and petroleum have dwindled alarmingly. Without these resources our whole way of life would be changed. More than two-thirds of the energy in the United States is supplied by underground oil and natural gas. The list of things petroleum does would be almost endless, and iron and copper are essential in the making of everyday objects.

The suggestions for relieving shortages include digging deeper mines, utilizing less rich deposits previously by-passed and substituting plastics for minerals whenever possible. The best hope, still, lies in locating more deposits; but they are not easily located, for the sand, gravel or rock appearing on the surface may bear little relationship to the deeply hidden minerals. Geophysicists, geobotanists, geochemists, mining geologists and engineers have a variety of techniques and tools, and industrialists are calling upon scientists more and more often to determine whether an area is worth developing.

The Labrador Mining and Engineering Company had a lease on a wilderness area in Canada which seemed to promise iron ore for North America's hungry steel mills. However, mining the ore and transporting it would necessitate building railroads, dams, power houses and docks on the St. Lawrence River, and unless investors could be assured that the deposit would yield 300,000,000 or 400,000,000 tons of ore, the financial risk would be too great. In a running battle with nature, and at great expense, the Labrador Company flew in scientists, supplies and equipment for a survey. The geologists who explored and appraised the rugged terrain later recommended going ahead with the project, and it proved to be as profitable as the survey promised.

To improve their techniques of detection, geologists sometimes undertake specialized surveys for strictly scientific purposes. In 1959 a geochemical unit from the United States Geological Survey cruised up and down Nevada in a squat green truck affectionately dubbed the Squash Bug. The Survey team aimed to map the area geochemically and to standardize techniques for geologists and untrained prospectors in remote areas.

Since previous experimentation had demonstrated that chemical analysis of surface soil often gives answers to what lies below, soil analysis occupied much of the Survey team's time. After measuring and sieving samples, the geochemists carried them to the luxury laboratory housed in the Squash Bug. Working with ultraviolet lamps, purified water, beakers, bottles, funnels and filters, they made extensive tests.

Simplest of these was the colorimetric test. In colorimetric testing a dried, crushed sample of oil is dropped into a graduated test tube. Different acids or reagents may be added, but a typical procedure is to introduce ammonium citrate and shake the mixture vigorously. The geochemist then adds dithizone, which makes specific color appear. By slight modifications, for example changing the acidity, the geochemist can tell which metal is present by the color revealed in the test tube. Its intensity gives some idea as to the amount.

For use by amateur prospectors the U.S.G.S. geochemists devised a colorimetric set resembling a junior chemistry set. Small and portable, it contains acids, unbreakable polyethylene bottles and an instruction sheet. The sample of soil can be identified by comparing it with a plastic color scale. The procedure is so simple that even an uneducated Alaskan sourdough can use it. Analysis by spectograph produces the same results, but that instrument is expensive and bulky and requires trained operators.

Colorimetric testing is only approximately correct, but it does give a good idea of the extent of a deposit and the method is cheap, easy and quick. To analyze forty samples of soil supposedly containing zinc might take up to four days by ordinary methods. A geochemist using colorimetric techniques could do it in about three hours. This type of testing also eliminates expensive, useless drilling.

Industrial and university laboratories, as well as the United States Geological Survey, are making advances in chemical analysis of rocks, soil and water. Already geochemists have located valuable resources beneath areas written off as wastelands—jungles, deserts and swamps. They have also found additional deposits in land supposedly worked out.

At a western lead mine in 1956 miners reported that it was useless to continue operations, since they had encountered only barren limestone; but geochemists found the limestone had intruded for only a short distance. Twelve feet away lay valuable deposits of lead.

Plants may also serve as indicators of underground minerals. For a long time scientists had known that the root system of plants pumps up needed minerals from the soil beneath them. But added research has revealed a striking relationship between certain plants and metals. Violets often thrive above deposits of zinc. California poppies grow larger and thicker in regions with a concentration of copper. Copper itself may not be the stimulant, but phosphate, a good plant nutrient, is normally in a more soluble state near copper deposits. Such plants known to have an affinity for mineralized areas are referred to by geobotanists as pathfinder plants.

Mrs. Helen Cannon, geobotanist for the United States Geological

Survey Office in Denver, Colorado, discovered one of these pathfinder plants while on a survey trip led by her husband, a geologist, when one of their pack horses died mysteriously. Mrs. Cannon, suspecting that locoweed had been the killer, conducted intensive research. She found that one species of locoweed absorbs selenium, which is toxic to animals. Selenium is an element usually found in association with uranium. Mrs. Cannon reasoned that areas in which locoweed flourished might have underlying uranium deposits. In 1952 a team of scientists she headed located in Utah four rich uranium deposits underlying islands of selenium-absorbing locoweed. Subsequently, miners in that state corroborated the close association between locoweed and uranium.

To get samples for research to improve their prediction techniques, geobotanists wander among the dunes and sagebrush of sunbaked deserts, slashing off cactus needles and mesquite twigs. Geobotanical forecasting promises to play a more prominent role in the future than it has in the past, although at present plants are not always reliable indicators.

Scientists trained in structural geology study a different set of clues when they go prospecting. They look to rocks for their answers. As soon as a geologist knows the family of a specimen, he knows much about its mineral possibilities. There is, for example, a close association between igneous rocks and minerals. Igneous rocks formed when superheated rocks beneath the surface of the earth became fluid and flowed into cracks and fissures. These compounds cooled and crystallized in various ways, some becoming lead, others gold, copper, or zinc.

If the quest is for petroleum, geologists know there are three essentials—source beds, reservoir beds and traps. Shale or limestone may be an indication of source beds, but reservoir beds are more likely to consist of sandstone, which is more porous. Geologists explain that rock pressure in the past squeezed fluids, including particles of oil, out of shale or limestone source beds into the pores of sandstone.

Although some oil may still appear in the shale or limestone, its removal is not always profitable. Drilling ventures in oil or kerogen shale have in the past produced as little as a pint of oil per ton of shale.

Underground oil floats on the top of any water it encounters and may eventually rise to a point where it seeps out at the surface, or it may collect in underground traps or small pools. Traps sometimes form when the earth buckles along a fault or when porous rock folds upward. In some cases, oil is held down by the presence of nonporous rocks. Upfolded arched rocks or anticlines often give away the secret of buried oil, but although some anticlines appear on the surface, many lie miles below.

To take a look at subsurface formations, geologists, if possible, descend into old wells, pits, and mines in the region under investigation. They examine drill cuttings and look for stains, odor and fluorescence under violet light, any one of which might be a sign of petroleum.

Large-scale, well-financed surveys conducted for an industry use the services of both geologists and geophysicists. In 1960 several Canadian and United States oil companies pooled their resources for an elaborate survey of oil potentialities in parts of Canada and Alaska.

The scientists, transported to isolated spots by launch, plane or helicopter, camped in tents and often worked a sixteen-hour day. In the early stages of the survey, geologists checked surface features that might give clues to oil trapped beneath the tundra. Later, geophysicists used magnetometers, delicate instruments which register the amount of magnetic attraction. These magnetic devices are based on the principle that in each of three great classes of rocks, wide variations exist in ore content and hence in magnetism. Metamorphic and igneous rocks, in which ores are most likely to be found, are usually more magnetic than sedimentary ones.

Magnetometer readings from instruments set up in a number of points are plotted on a map with lines drawn through points of equal magnetic intensity. It takes skill to operate the magnetometer and interpret results intelligently. Ore very often underlies the area of greatest intensity, but there are always unknowns, such as atmospheric variations, which may cause erroneous conclusions.

119

PROSPECTING FROM THE AIR

Geologists conducting the Alaskan survey also used magnetometers towed by planes or helicopters flying along a series of parallel lines. The magnetometers were paired with sonar transmitting devices. With transmitted signals fanning out to the ground and reflecting waves back to the magnetometer, ore bodies as deep as two thousand feet below the surface were detected. When a magnetometer registered nothing at all, the scientists conducted no further tests in the area.

The Alaska survey party also made extensive use of seismic soundings up and down the Mackenzie River. Some conventional methods, such as drilling to bring up samples, were neglected because of the difficulties in transporting equipment, but also because of the permafrost, an ice layer lying only inches below the surface. The expense of flying in supplies—one watermelon cost fourteen dollars and eighty cents—the vicious mosquitoes and the undependable communications handicapped the scientists. But the expedition accomplished what it had set out to do.

On many surveys for underground resources, gravimeters are used. Underlying rocks vary slightly in density and the gravitational attraction is higher over rocks of higher density. Gravimeters are very efficient in locating salt domes, often found near good petroleum traps. With a portable gravimeter, a team of geologists or geophysicists can measure as many as fifty stations in a day. However, the readings require much calculation and correction because the instruments are sensitive to changes in altitude and latitude and other variable factors.

Geophysicists also judge the properties of rocks by passing an electrical current through them to reveal their conductivity and resistivity. Bodies of massive sulphides such as galena or pyrite are better conductors than rocks, whereas quartz veins are usually poorer.

Geiger counters have been very useful in locating uranium. A Geiger counter contains a special type of electronic tube which permits pulsations of electric currents to pass through it when it is bombarded by gamma rays. The pulsations are amplified electronically so that each makes a click in the head phones of the scientist. The rate of clicking is a measure of the relative abundance of radioactive materials nearby giving off gamma rays.

There is no one foolproof method for detecting subsurface metals, minerals, or petroleum. Sometimes nothing comes of a quest. One mining company relying on an aerial survey accepted magnetometer readings which indicated a terrain likely to be productive of oil in a hilly region of Canada. The company fitted out a ground party with expensive equipment, including drilling rigs. About three weeks and two thousand dollars later, they scuttled the project. Drill holes revealed only a graphite deposit buried under a hundred feet or more of glacial debris.

But occasionally a find exceeds the wildest dream of the sponsors. In December of 1955, Scottish geologist Alexander Clark, working in the vicinity of Mt. Nimba in Liberia, cabled his employer, "I have found a mountain of iron ore." Research by other geologists confirmed his optimism. It is estimated that Mt. Nimba will yield at least 250,000 tons of rich iron ore.

After petroleum, iron, copper, or some other metal has been located, the prospector or mining company wants to know the approximate size of the deposit, whether it lies so deep that it will be expensive to mine, and what yield can be expected over a period of years.

Such questions can usually be answered by a mining geologist or engineer, or both. The position of a mining geologist is about midway between the field of theoretical geology with its kindred sciences and the highly technical arts of mining and metallurgy. If the questions are being answered for a petroleum industry, the geologist, who may have been a member of the survey party, makes further use of gravimeters, magnetometers, seismometers and drilling cores. But he narrows his research to areas where the survey had indicated rocks of an age and type to contain oil.

After every scrap of information is pieced together, the geologist draws various kinds of maps—topography and contour ones showing surface features, and subsurface ones indicating the kinds of rocks and their formations and the probable location of oil traps.

Meanwhile, the petroleum engineer studies scale models built to simulate states of rock porosity, oil viscosity and pressure in the field to be developed. With the help of electric computer machines and complex mathematical formulas he estimates the yield, operating costs and profits that can be expected over a period of years. It is up to the geologist or engineer to indicate exactly where wells should be sunk. Sometimes a trial shaft is drilled. Not all the basic geological requirements may be discernible before drilling sites are chosen, but the more there are of them, the greater the certainty of oil.

The geologist or engineer is not always right. His instruments have informed him of conditions favorable for the presence of oil, but they have not indicated whether oil actually exists. Promising petroleum traps may fail to yield oil because of poor porosity. Oil may have migrated before the anticline formed.

Underground Riches

To keep pace with demands for metals and minerals, especially for iron and petroleum, more accurate search methods will have to be developed. Geologists long for instruments that will X-ray the earth and show exactly what lies underground, but until such dreams come true they will have to aim at more accurate interpretation of findings from the instruments they have. There is a need for improved geochemical testing and for novel processes of extraction to make usable the less rich deposits of minerals and fuels.

But even without adequate instruments, geologists have reduced the hazards of the oil and mineral business. These scientific treasure hunters have aided many a baffled prospector and chalked up some spectacular successes in locating essential metals and minerals. By helping to unearth basic resources they have played an important role in our industrial economy. It can be expected that in the future geologists will supply many more answers, for many of them seem to be imbued with the idea that faith added to knowledge can do almost anything. To acquire that knowledge they will willingly go forth to live in tents, trailers or tin shacks in areas populated mostly with poisonous snakes and wild beasts.

Geologists, geophysicists and petroleum engineers are engaged in a rugged but fascinating game of hide-and-go-seek with Nature—a game in which they hope to bring up the remaining treasures from Earth's rocky crust. The assurance that they can open for their profession and their country new jobs, new techniques, new wealth and new horizons makes the struggle worth while to most survey scientists.

13

Miners with Aqualungs

After World War I a German chemist named Fritz Haber conceived the idea of paying his nation's war debt by making the sea yield up its treasure. In samples of sea water subjected to chemical analysis, he had often detected tiny particles of gold. Why not reclaim this precious metal from the sea? Haber raised funds for a ship, a laboratory and a filtration plant, but the cost of extraction exceeded the value of the gold recovered.

Critics called Haber a wild-eyed treasure hunter, but he was right in believing that immense riches lie buried in the sea. Gold, among other metals absorbed by micro-organisms, is carried to the ocean floor, where it is dissolved and taken up into the water.

Alarmed by the depletion of minerals on land, government and industry have turned more and more to the hidden resources of the sea, and officials are bombarding scientists with questions. They want to know where the minerals of the sea are concentrated, how they can be extracted, whether the cost would be prohibitive and how claims could be staked out underwater. As on land, the first problem is locating the resources.

One of the earliest explorations for underwater oil was undertaken by Captain Jacques Cousteau in 1954, at the request of the British Petroleum Company, Ltd. To equip the *Calypso* for the venture, Cousteau installed marine counterparts of instruments used for underground detection—seismometers, gravimeters and magnetometers. In the Gulf of Suez, Cousteau and his oil hunters, using aqualungs, tested their equipment. Then the *Calypso* sped on toward the Persian Gulf and the Pirate Coast.

Cousteau wanted first to find underseas "domes," since such formations often denote the presence of petroleum. From geologists he had learned that domes had originated when leaves, twigs, seaweed and carcasses of animals, squid, sturgeon, sharks and whales had sunk to the muddy ooze of the ocean floor. Then rivers emptying into the sea covered the deposits with sand, silt and clay, and pressure, heat and the action of bacteria transformed the sediments into rocks. Converted to gas and oil, the organic materials exerted pressure upward, in mounds. Cousteau was interested in ordinary salt domes, too, since there is always the possibility of oil deposits in the sediments close to them. To locate these, the *Calypso* crew used a gravity meter installed on a track on the deck so it could be run over the side and lowered to the bottom. Electric cables connected it to the control room. As soon as the meter hit bottom, it started to relay information. A slight deviation in a reading might indicate an underwater dome containing black gold; so, when an irregularity was noted, divers with aqualungs went down to investigate.

To get samples for later analysis, the divers used picks, hammers and chisels as geologists do on land. There were marked differences, however. Allowance had to be made for pressure, and while the divers worked, a shark cage stood nearby in case of emergency.

All samples of rock that divers brought up from below were tagged with the exact location and date of their finding. The chief geologist analyzed some of them in the *Calypso*'s laboratory; others were bagged and put aside for a more leisurely and detailed examination by a laboratory in London.

At intervals the *Calypso* crew dropped a coring bomb, a half ton of solid steel with a hard coring pipe in its nose, to drill out rock samples from the ocean floor. One day when the winch brought up the bomb, it had no pipe, no drill, and, of course, no sample.

Two divers went down with a compressed-air drill, hoping that they could cut out a sample by hand. At the site of the coring, the pipe lay twisted in a Z shape. The rock was so hard that the drill just bounced on the ocean bottom. Cousteau and his assistants were discouraged. The expedition had already been costly, and the loss of equipment added to the expense. Now in an area that seemed to be promising, they couldn't even seem to bring up a sample. Finally, two divers went down with a chisel and a sledge hammer.

They returned with only a few slivers of rock. Sheepishly they turned them over to the chief geologist who took them to the laboratory; but after a while he emerged grinning. "Look at that," he said, handing to Cousteau a fragment of rock and a jeweler's magnifying monocle. "Nummulite shell. When you find that, it's a pretty fair sign of oil."

Despite drilling mishaps, sea squalls and sharks, the Cousteau party met with considerable success during its two-month stay in the Persian Gulf. Four hundred samplings of the sea floor proved the presence of oil. Since then, treasure hunters with aqualungs have located even more valuable deposits.

Sometimes important minerals can be located by dredging. In 1957, ships from the Scripps Institution of Oceanography dredged up quantities of potato-shaped lumps ranging from half an inch to ten inches in diameter. Dirty brown or earthy black in color, they could be easily scratched by a knife. These nodules were made up of a high percentage of manganese and small amounts of iron, nickel, cobalt and copper. In water they reacted quickly to dissolved oxygen and precipitated on anything handy as manganese dioxide.

Manganese is much prized by industries manufacturing products where strength is needed without unusual weight. Lighter than aluminum, yet possessing remarkable strength, it is a vital ingredient for steel. Manganese also enters into the production of metal ladders; bicycles; and the wheels, engine parts and landing gear of aircraft. Every big plane contains about half a ton of manganese.

At present the United States produces only about ten per cent of the manganese it needs. If the underseas nodules scattered fairly uniformly on the ocean floor were lying about on land, they would be snapped up for commercial mining companies. But thousands of feet of overlying sea water make a formidable barrier and the possibility of dredging for the nodules has been discussed but discarded.

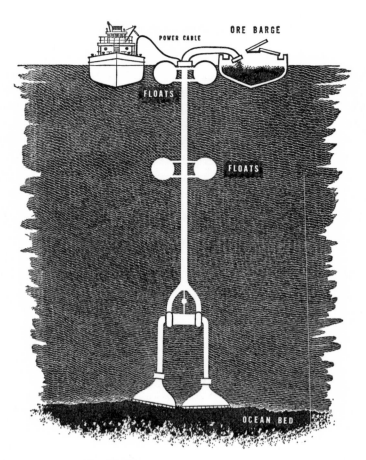

DEEP-SEA VACUUM CLEANER

Curious as to the possibility of using a specially designed machine to recover manganese, Scripps oceanographers turned the problem over to John Mero, a graduate student at the Berkeley campus of the University of California. After several years of study, he made a suggestion for a kind of underwater vacuum cleaner.

Most of the weight of Mero's device would be supported by buoyant tanks set a few hundred feet down to avoid the turbulent surface layers of the water. These would house the principal motors as well.

Nodules scooped up by suction arms would be dumped by a hydraulic dredge onto a barge. The vacuum cleaner procedure would be too expensive for manganese alone. However, it might be feasible if used in a close-to-shore area with concentrated deposits of manganese in combination with cobalt and nickel.

That the idea of vacuuming the sea bed is not too fantastic is being proved by a submarine mining venture off the coast of Southwest Africa. Aimed at securing diamonds, the project is sponsored by two American underwater pipeline experts. From each of two tugs, two large-diameter rubber hose pipes are lowered to the sea bed. When the pipes fill with water, a number of air jets at the bottom of each pump air into the sediment with great force.

As the soil is disturbed by the air, it whirls about and moves up the pipe. The outside pressure of the ocean forces the soil, and possibly diamonds with it, to the top, where processing and sorting take place on the deck of a barge. Worthless soil is dumped overboard.

Geologists have long contended that diamonds found on the West African coast originally came from the bed of the sea and were washed ashore. It seems reasonable to suppose that some remained. If the vacuuming process brings up diamonds, they will mean substantial revenue for its African sponsors.

Less valuable than diamonds but still necessary and valuable are deposits of bromine. A brown corrosive metal, bromine is a vital constituent of chemicals needed for dyestuffs, drugs, aircraft fire extinguishers and photographic films. In the nineteen hundred and twenties, the demand for bromine soared with the development of anti-knock gasoline, which required ethylene dibromide.

The problem in extracting this metal from the sea was that it might take as much as twenty-five hundred gallons of sea water to yield a pound of bromine. Chemists and engineers worked out a plan for locating a factory on a promontory with a water intake on one side and a discharge on the other. Through application of chemical engineering, the bromine was removed and unwanted water was returned to the sea. Eighty per cent of the bromine used in the United States today comes from the ocean.

At present the underseas product most wanted is petroleum. Scientists have played an important role not only in locating the oil but in devising schemes for extracting it. Before recommending a site for erecting a drilling rig, the geologist needs to be sure that it will provide safe conditions for personnel and that it will justify the expense. The cost of an offshore drilling platform—which must rest on deeply driven piles to withstand the violence of wind and water —is upwards of two million dollars. This is exclusive of the cost of actual drilling.

Geologists and engineers participated in every stage of the planning for Rincon, an artificial island built off the California coast between Ventura and Santa Barbara by the Richfield Oil Corporation. Wells pumping oil from beneath the sea now puncture the surface of its rock foundation, which is pyramided up to an acre of land well above the reach of high tides. A causeway connects Rincon with the mainland.

On the what and where of minerals in the ocean, scientists have provided many answers, although there is a need for more detailed and accurate surveys. Claims made by some chemists that there is enough gold in the sea to make every inhabitant of the world wealthy may be extravagant, but it is entirely possible that the ocean may yield more minerals than the land. Manganese and cobalt used in making special steels are so plentiful that mining them on even a modest scale could break the world market.

Geologists have reported that the ocean is a vast reservoir of copper, zinc, tin and uranium. There is also a tremendous amount of salt. Common as it may seem, salt is nonetheless essential to the making of glass, tires, dyes and soap. It is used in the processes of petroleum recovery, refrigeration and metallurgy. Industries utilize salt to cure hides, pack fish, preserve meats and flavor food.

If sea water can be enclosed in shallow ponds the sun and wind separate the salt out by the simple process of evaporation. In manmade solar evaporation plants salt is recovered through a combination of sun and a series of ponds, in each of which the salt becomes a little more concentrated until it is finally deposited in a crystallizing pond.

Sea mining of copper, zinc, tin or gold would have one great advantage over land mining. Minerals taken from the land cannot be replaced; those removed from the ocean can be. Submarine volcanoes discharge boron, chlorine and sulphur. Every stream or river emptying into the sea brings a new supply of metals dissolved from rock, soil and corroding metals. Minerals leach out of underseas rocks and eroding coastlines. An added dividend from the development of deep-sea deposits would be an alternative source of supply if foreign sources became unavailable for one reason or another.

However, although strides are being made in the underwater mining of petroleum, the efforts to extract mineral wealth have been feeble. One of the major problems is that the ocean wealth is spread so thinly. Chemists have found that iodine salts are so dilute in seawater they scarcely show a trace on analysis.

Part of the economic problem lies in the fact that the final product would be worth less than the cost of pumping the sea water. There are twenty-five tons of gold in every cubic mile of the sea. That's a good deal of gold. But extraction processes, while workable, cost more than the recovered gold is worth. For technical reasons a factory handling something over a million gallons of water a minute is about as large a unit as can be conveniently operated. Using this as a standard production unit, experts estimate that to supply the nation's needs for critical minerals at the 1957 rate of consumption it would take sixty-three factories for fluorine compounds and eight hundred thousand for copper.

Those who would mine the sea are also confronted by legal problems. Who owns the minerals under the high seas? How could a mining company or nation stake a claim and be guaranteed a lease? Until some international agency takes over jurisdiction and establishes rules to govern this common treasure for the world, claims will be meaningless.

But as the ores available on land become scarcer and of poorer quality, men will turn more and more to the sea. Already oil derricks are wading out into the waters above the continental shelves to reclaim the oil in the oozes and domes located by geological prospectors who knew how to interpret what they saw on the ocean floor. Tomorrow's great strikes may well be submarine ones.

Scientists intent on making the sea give up its treasures are supplying ingenious suggestions. They believe the concentrating processes of animal and plants of the sea can be put to better use. Iodine, for example, is dilute in water but seaweeds concentrate its salts to such an extent that they are a good source of commercial iodine. The same venturesome courage, scientific curiosity and clear-headed analysis that led marine geologists to locate these rich resources can lead to new ways of utilizing them.

14

Water for a Thirsty World

Rich as it is in water resources, the United States is not keeping pace with the thirst of its expanding population. Shortages already exist in some sections of the country. According to figures presented to the Senate Committee on Water Resources, roughly a third of the nation will have insufficient water by 1980.

In a large measure the search for life has become identified with the search for water. Lack of water can close factories and put workers out of jobs; it can destroy the productive capacity of farms. It is essential to the life of the individual, the community and the nation. The big question is, is there enough water for the future? There will be if new sources can be located, if present supplies can be conserved, and if the "have" areas share with the "have-not" areas.

These "ifs" are being intensively examined by geophysicists, geologists, chemists, and a relatively new group of specialists called hydrologists. The work of a hydrologist ranges from the study of origin, properties, and distribution of water to the design and operation of projects for the control and use of it. Geologists concentrate on rocks; hydrologists concentrate on the pore spaces and soluble constituents and utilize principles of hydraulics, physics and chemistry as well as geology.

If water shortages are to be overcome, the causes must be determined. Through research, scientists have learned that natural processes impose many limitations on supply. The most obvious of these, drought, can cause severe shortages in specific areas. After three years of little rain in the northeastern section of the United States, beachside hotels during the summer of 1949 had to put a ban on bath water. Bellboys carried water to guests in buckets. During the same period New York City imposed fines for leaky plumbing and appealed to citizens to use as little water as possible.

Even where rainfall is more abundant, almost two-thirds of the moisture is quickly taken up again into the atmosphere through transpirations from trees, plants, animals and human beings, but also through evaporation. It is estimated that 893,000,000 gallons of water evaporate each day from Lake Mead in Nevada.

Salt encroachment complicates water shortages even in areas far from any sea. Rain and snow absorbed by the ground gradually dissolve the soil's sodium, calcium, manganese and potassium, the original source of salts. If the ground water is depleted, the concentration of minerals and salts may become so strong that the water has an acrid taste and is detrimental to crops, cattle and men.

Hydrological studies show that the greatest strains on water supply are imposed by agriculture and industry. Many vegetables, if irrigated, need a million or more gallons of water per acre per season of production. It takes forty-three gallons to produce one pound of oranges. A big steer gulps down thirty to forty gallons of water a day.

Certain types of industry consume tremendous amounts of water. The Aero-jet General Corporation in Sacramento uses up to fifteen thousand gallons of water a minute many times a day for each test firing of liquid rocket fuels. Some of the water is reclaimed, but much of it turns to steam and evaporates. To preprocess a ton of steel requires sixty-five thousand gallons of water. Two and a half gallons go into the production of one phonograph record. Oil refineries and chemical, pulp and paper concerns make big demands.

Scientists are alarmed by the quantity of water made unfit for drinking because of pollution. Sewage, acids, chemicals, grease and industrial waste all contaminate a stream. Sometimes water used for cooling in an industrial process may be returned so hot to a stream that it stops the bacterial decomposition of sewage and kills fish, thus adding to pollution.

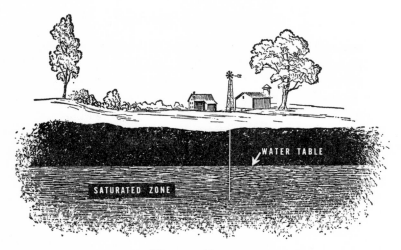

WATER TABLE

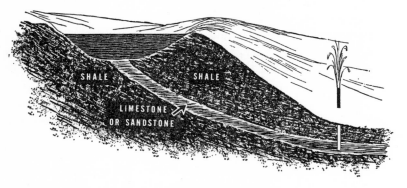

AQUIFER

Frequently when geologists or hydrologists are called in for consultation on a problem of shortage, they find the cause is the lowering of the water table.

If rocks beneath the soil are permeable, the water sinks to considerable depths through cracks, crevices and pores. Permeable rocks constantly flooded by moisture from above may become so full that water can no longer sink downwards. The level below which the rocks are full of water is called the water table, and the basins and natural reservoirs underneath it are known as aquifers.

Their surplus water courses off in underground streams, which may, like surface ones, flow to the ocean.

In wet regions where the water table lies high, prolonged rainfall causes it to rise. If the overlying rocks are porous, the water then gushes up as a spring at the surface. Drought will have the opposite effect. A water table may sink from a few inches to over fifty feet.

To get information on the mysterious ways of underground water tables, geologists and hydrologists descend into old wells and mine holes, bring up samples of earth in cores, and drill test wells. They have found that continued overpumping can have as disastrous an effect as drought. Water tables have dropped steadily in some sections of Arizona, New Mexico, Texas and California. Because rainfall is slight in these areas, there is little hope of replenishment.

Formerly some seepage from streams increased underground supplies, but most of these are now dammed into artificial lakes. Hydrologists warn that practically all the underground water being pumped in Arizona is a draft on an account not being renewed. Many wells are nearing depletion. The result could be increased desert areas.

Overpumping also causes salty sea water to creep into wells of coastal cities. At Texas City the source of sweet water, because of the presence of saturated underground sands, seemed unending. Over a period of years, however, industries overpumped. Water in several big wells dropped to a hundred feet or so below sea level. Fresh water flowing through underground layers could no longer push back Gulf of Mexico water. Ocean brine seeping into wells produced a distasteful flavor and snarled industrial operations in a plant constructed to use sweet water.

If withdrawals from ground water areas are so excessive that the water level drops, then filth from sewage or industrial operations can sluice into wells. There have been instances of insecticides and detergents in domestic water waste finding their way into wells of drinking water and poisoning them. Tulsa, Oklahoma, had to stop using Arkansas River water because it was too badly polluted with oil field brine.

Water supply would be a critical problem even without the population explosion. During the last decade nine million persons moved into seven western states already short of water. Estimates on per capita consumption vary from city to city and season to season, but may run as high as fifteen thousand gallons a day if water necessary to provide electric power for appliances is figured in. Water usage is being pushed upward by the popularity of swimming pools, air conditioners, washing machines and garbage grinders.

Another effect concentration of population has on water supply is to diminish it by roofing the land. Underground sources are covered by building and paving. Instead of being absorbed, the water that falls on these areas is drained off so that such springs as once existed cannot be replenished.

Confronted by the burgeoning demands of agriculture, industry, and city living, scientists are exploring many possibilities for increasing and conserving water supply. These range from artificial rainmaking to retardation of evaporation through covering reservoirs with thin, noncontaminating, chemical film. Conservation measures such as building dams and replanting forests and grasslands to retain moisture are important. But these are answers related to surface features.

The happiest solution to the problem of inadequate water would be location of sources hitherto untapped. Since surface sources have been thoroughly explored, geologists and hydrologists have turned to the underground. On the basis of topography and findings from instruments which provide a kind of subsurface mapping, scientists can evaluate ground-water deposits.

One system of detection makes use of shallow seismic refraction. Small charges of explosives detonated just below ground level create vibrations that bounce back and are measured on a seismometer. This method indicates dips or troughs in which water may collect.

Sometimes a surface appearance betrays the presence of underground water. Leadville, a growing mountain town in Colorado, found its water supply becoming inadequate. An hydrologist called in to locate a new source observed water flowing from an old abandoned mine tunnel. Tracing it to its underground source, he found a supply that could meet community needs.

Geologists have for some time used an electrical resistivity method for locating water. This process is based on the theory that the resistivity of water differs from that of rocks. The New Mexico Institute of Mining and Technology, operating on this principle, devised a kind of prospecting technique known as induced polarization.

In this method geophysicists unreel high voltage wires and attach them to electrodes driven into the ground at a spacing of several hundred feet. A direct current flowing through these from a generator housed in a truck energizes the ground. Two other electrodes nearby convey the impulses through wires connected to recording equipment. As soon as the current is shut off, the rate of decay of the voltage induced into the ground is measured by the tracings of an automatic pen which draws curves on the recorder. Then the whole operation is repeated with electrodes spaced farther apart.

If the curve on the recorder is flat, this means no water and tests are discontinued. But if the curve rises steeply, the geophysicist continues with further readings and tests which predict with some degree of accuracy the depth of water, the boundaries of the natural reservoir, or aquifer, the probable yield of water and its degree of purity. This induced polarization method is effective, but it is expensive because it requires specialized equipment and a three-man crew. It is also time-consuming. To spot-check an area of thirty square miles would require a month.

Induced polarization and seismic refraction are used primarily for detecting rainwater which has percolated into the earth. Some geologists believe that there is also an accumulation of water from centuries past which rises up from below. A few believe that under certain conditions water is actually formed deep in the earth's crust.

When Stephen Riess, a former mining engineer, advanced the theory that hydrogen and oxygen coming together at high temperatures and under vast pressures could produce water, getting new water from deep-down rocks seemed a wild flight of imagination to most scientists. Riess was accused of being a charlatan. Unperturbed, he continued laboratory tests on rock samples and then through examination of terrain located rocks in which he expected to find fissures containing underground water.

Despite his unorthodox theories and techniques, Riess succeeded in sinking wells into solid granite which spouted water at the rate of two or three thousand gallons a minute. He developed wells with potable water in arid sections of California, on the Mojave Desert. At the request of Prime Minister Ben Gurion he went to Israel, where he located sites for wells on the Negev Desert. Chemical analyses of rocks, water samples, drilling cores and dissolved gases in Riess wells showed that water had not percolated down through the soil.

Since it is not anticipated that the nation's supply will be greatly expanded by the location of new sources of ground water, scientists are seeking ways and means to make the best possible use of available resources. A number of projects have centered around the reclamation of brackish water now deemed unsuitable for human use.

Chemists and physicists have come forth with various processes for producing sweet water from salinized—evaporation by solar energy and freeze conversion are two methods—but in many cases expense has limited their usage to such isolated instances as an industrial operation on a desert or a military installation on a remote island. Several hopeful projects are now underway.

In one novel process, originated by Kopper's Company, Inc., the pure water is changed into a solid just long enough to separate it from the salty bath in which it floats. By a combination of heat, chemicals, and condensation chilled salt water is separated from the sweet.

A different type of desalination project is in operation in Buckeye, Arizona, where residents wrestled for years with the problems of hard, salty-tasting water. Twenty-six wells were drilled from time to time, only to be abandoned. Residents paid out large sums of money for bottled water and for extra detergents to launder their clothes. Scientists at last solved the community's potable-water shortage with an electrodialysis plant. Here the water is subjected to a current which causes positive salt ions to move into one chamber and negative ions into another. A high percentage of the magnesium, sodium and calcium flow off in a rejected portion of the water, leaving fresh water behind.

Another practical experiment in desalting is being carried out in Freeport, Texas. The pilot plant to make salty Gulf of Mexico water potable was built by the Interior Department's Office of Saline Water. The plant is, in effect, a series of twelve stills. Cloudy green sea water, alive with tiny mullet and crabs, is pumped into an intake tank; and then, after filtering, it passes into the first still, which heats the water to the boiling point. This produces a hot, desalted vapor which flows into and heats the second still, and so on. As the vapor gives up its heat it is condensed as pure water, to be pumped into the city mains and flow sweet and pure from the taps. Four gallons of sea water make three of fresh, plus a gallon of concentrated brine that is returned to the Gulf. The plant provides Freeport with a fourth of its total daily fresh water needs at a reasonable expense.

Desalination will play a role in supplying coastal cities with water, but scientists do not see it as a magical solution for the national problem. It requires a large amount of cheap power and the cost of pumping water inland would be prohibitive.

Scientists are also making studies of the best possible use of water for agricultural purposes. In some instances hydrologists have convinced farmers that less water would give the same yield. Cotton farmers in California now produce four times as much cotton with an acre foot of water as they did in 1940.

On the whole, however, suggestions made by hydrologists and chemists, such as the use of treated effluent for watering crops, have not met with enthusiasm. Some hydrologists believe the only solution for arid sections is industrialization. They recommend a local shift away from water-consuming agriculture to industries that could use and re-use available water.

In some communities hydrologists have helped eliminate objections to industrial usage of water by suggesting that uncontaminated water from plants be discharged back into a stream in a cooled condition so plant and animal life can remain undisturbed. Head-on collisions between industry and water shortage have in some instances been met by re-using the supply available. At Bishop, Texas, a big celanese plant re-uses water as much as fifty times.

An industry can save time, money, expense, and strained public relations if before locating in a community it calls on geologists and hydrologists to supply data on the quantity of water available and the possibilities for its re-use. The quality of the water is also important, since alkalinity, hardness and corrosiveness may have an effect on the product. One cannery discovered, after locating in a community, that the hard water made the peas as hard as buckshot.

In many instances, large industrial plants have been built in areas where water seemed abundant but after a time became inadequate. During World War II, the stepped-up production at plants in one community located on the Ohio River so depleted the water supply that factories were threatened with a shutdown. Then the industrial leaders asked for a survey to be made by the Ground Water Division of the U.S. Geological Survey. Had the geologists been consulted in the first place, they could have foretold that the wells could not support the demands made on them because of the nature of subsurface rocks in the area. All the geologists could do under the circumstances was recommend cooling towers and the relocation of some of the wells closer to the Ohio River. The plants survived, but the relocation cost millions of dollars.

Hydrologists and geologists know that the most productive wells are located over aquifers and underground streams, but locating the water is not enough. The scientist must ask himself, "Will this water be fit to drink? Is it likely that minerals or salt could intrude? Will continual pumping deplete it? Does the aquifer have a means of recharging through moisture from above or some underground source?"

Replenishment is directly linked with percolation. Where the underflow is in very porous gravel or rock, replacement water can more readily come in than where wells tap underlying strata composed of tighter textures.

Combining geological data with his observation of the site, a study of previous wells in the area, and perhaps the digging of a test well, the geologist or hydrologist can indicate where a well should be located. He can also give advice on the kind of well it should be, and to what depth it should be drilled. He can predict the yield in gallons per minute and the chemical qualities of the water.

Proper geological evaluation of an area can save the prospective buyer of land possible disappointment and financial loss. A geologist can give the developer of a subdivision an estimate on how many wells could be drilled in the area without dangerously depleting the ground supply.

Although geologists can forecast the results of overpumping or of too many wells in an area, they have no way of controlling abuses. In 1923, wells in the Roosevelt artesian basin near Roswell, New Mexico, had dropped so low that some stopped yielding water completely. After some farmers had abandoned their land because of lack of water, the United States Geological Survey was called in to make a study.

Making the rounds, geologists found some wells still in action, flowing unchecked and wasting valuable water, and a number of wells had leaky casing. The situation was relieved when scientists located another level of water that could be pumped to supplement the artesian flow, but they warned that if the overuse continued unchecked, the supplementary supply would soon be inadequate. Partly as the result of these investigations and recommendations, the legislature passed laws controlling waste and restricting the use of ground water. New Mexico now has one of the most advanced sets of regulations on the use of water of all the states of the Union.

Hydrologists and geologists, who have a better picture of the national water resources than anyone else, believe that there is enough water for the future if what there is is kept pure, and if it is used wisely. The reduction of reservoir evaporation, the location of new sources and desalination projects can increase the available supply.

But the present situation is critical. A mounting population demands more and more water. Already industrial expansion in many communities is limited by lack of water. Kerogen shale deposits in Colorado which would yield immense quantities of oil cannot be processed because the water it would take is not available. Factories and military experimentation constantly increase the possibility of pollution. Atomic fallout, for example, could conceivably be absorbed by snow or rain and seep down to contaminate underground sources.

More legislation is needed to curb pollution, to curtail the reckless overuse of water and to insure protection against depletion. Some intelligent compromising will have to be done between sections of the country with adequate water supply and those with shortages. Too little is known about the overall water resources of the nation—yet trained hydrologists who could offer competent guidance on locating, controlling and utilizing American water resources, more important to the nation's welfare than astronauts, are small in numbers.

But even skilled scientists cannot solve the problem alone. Haphazard, blundering policies in the use of water must be abandoned. Scientists need the backing of an alert, informed, thinking public. Time is against us. Lack of water can turn our fertile fields into deserts and kill our nation as easily as war. Scientists can solve the problem of too little water, but only if other Americans realize that the job is also theirs.

15

Keys to the Past

Indians who lived near Shasta Lake in California many years ago believed that a magic pool in nearby Samwel Cave brought good fortune to those who drank of the waters. But few dared to go there, because they imagined that a giant who captured victims made the cave his home.

One day an Indian girl and a friend took torches and bravely entered the cave. As they groped through the dark passages, the girl in the lead suddenly screamed. Her companion heard a thud and then silence. Only mocking echoes came back when she called her friend by name. Terrified, the Indian maiden ran to her father for help. He and other braves returned to the cave, but failed to rescue the girl, who had fallen into an abyss that seemed bottomless.

In recent years when a group of paleontologists and archaeologists were exploring caves in the Shasta Lake area for whatever remains of early plant, human or animal life they might find, an Indian related to paleontologist John C. Meriam the story of Samwel Cave. Knowing that legends can lead to fossils, and that possibly he might find relics that would answer some paleontological puzzles, Meriam tried to persuade an Indian to lead him to the cave. When not one of them would go, he organized his own party.

Two trips into the interior netted nothing. On the third expedition, the paleontologists explored every dripping, narrow, twisting crawlway they could find. At last one passageway ended in an abyss deeper than the ladder the explorers carried. After workmen in their party extended it, the scientists drew straws to choose the one to make the descent. Scientist Furlong had hardly disappeared over the brink when he called, "Mountain lion down here!"

Meriam stood horror-struck, until he realized Furlong meant a fossilized one. On the floor of the abyss, where if there had ever been a pool it had dried up, Furlong found the skeleton of a girl as well as of the lion. Extending the research over a period of several days, the paleontologists ferreted out the tooth of a sloth and bones of unknown species of porcupines, squirrels, deer, foxes, raccoons and rabbits. There were also lime-encrusted bones of human beings who must have inhabited the cave thousands of years ago.

Relics such as those found in Samwel Cave answer many questions about the past. Even if they are fragmentary, fossilized plants and animals reveal much about the age when they were living, growing organisms. Although the fossils are dead, paleontology, which means literally the "science of ancient life," is far from dead. Research enables paleontologists to explain the evolution, distribution and relationship of present species, and paleontology has some very practical applications even in our industrialized world. A knowledge of fossils can be very valuable in locating mineral or petroleum deposits.

Scientists once thought fossils rare, but they now know that nearly all sedimentary rocks deposited in shallow lakes or streams contain them. Fossils also occur in accretions of phosphorous-rich rocks. To find the fossilized remains of animals and plants, paleontologists visit caves, coal mines and fossilized forests, split open rocks and probe pits and peat bogs.

In choosing a site for research, paleontologists may be assisted by Nature, construction companies, cowboys or laymen. Erosion along stream banks or ocean cliffs may expose long-concealed fossils. The bones of mastodons or tigers have sometimes been revealed by excavations for swimming pools, buildings or canals. Coyotes or ground squirrels burrowing in the ground occasionally paw out teeth or bones. When bringing home his cows, one Australian farmer detected bones of fossil kangaroos in a hillside pasture. The skull of a dinosaur reported by a Wyoming cowboy led to other important discoveries.

Occasionally scientists act on hunches in locating fossils. Swedish geologist Gunnar Andersson, while in China in 1917 as a mining adviser to the government, became more and more interested in the "dragons' bones" and teeth he saw in apothecaries' shops. When ground and taken in the form of tea, the bones supposedly cured anything from malaria to madness.

Andersson had read the writings of the Munich paleontologist Max Schlowwer who believed the so-called dragon bones might be remains of prehistoric animals. The Swedish geologist had a similar suspicion, but he could not get apothecaries to reveal the source of supply of their dragon bones.

Soliciting help from foreigners and missionaries in China, Andersson got some valuable hints. One missionary suggested digging in a red clay area where she had heard natives had recovered dragon teeth. Workmen hired by Andersson unearthed skulls of wolves and tigers, and the jaws of hyenas and rhinoceroses. The natives and the apothecaries called the bones and teeth of almost any animal dragon bones.

In the mines to which his work took him Andersson found the bones of extinct animals. His persistent research led in 1929 to the discovery of the fossilized man later known as Peking man.

One of the frustrations of field work is that paleontologists most often find damaged or incomplete specimens. After the death of an animal the soft parts are usually eaten by a marauder. Only the bones, shell, or hard outer covering survive. More often than not the paleontologists are confronted by a faint footprint, a few bones, or the shape or mold of a departed animal, but even such skimpy remains provide some answers.

By comparing its foot and hoof prints with similar marks made by living animal relatives paleontologists can classify a long-dead wanderer. In the prison yard at Carson City, Nevada, paleontologists identified footprints of mammoths, camels and sloths.

Taking molds of bones in rock can be a very useful technique.

Paleontologists used this method when they found a fossilized rhinoceros interred in a cliff at Blue Lake in the state of Washington. A lava flow had invaded the ancient lake and killed the beast, but water had cooled the magma before it incinerated him. Only the bones remained, but scientists made plaster of Paris duplicates of the body form molded in lava.

The most rewarding collection of fossils ever found in America was discovered in 1950 by a Christian Brother, G. Nicholas, and his students in Cumberland Cave about three miles northwest of Cumberland, Maryland. Perhaps "rediscovered" would be a more accurate word, since J. W. Gridley of the United States National Museum had visited the cave in 1912 and brought out bones of all sorts of animals from bats to mastodons. Because loose rock near the entrance made the access dangerous, the cave had had to be sealed, but Brother Nicholas and his students found a new entrance.

The discovery of the left half of the jaw of a giant grizzly bear convinced both teacher and pupils that the cave was worth further research. Brother Nicholas and the students excavated every weekend through the winter and spring of 1950–51. Digging was arduous and at times dangerous. In the cramped quarters students had to wear masks because of the foul air and great, choking clouds of dust.

Eventually, officials of the Western Maryland Railroad, which had a right-of-way across the top of the cave, promised to assist Brother Nicholas. Using a succession of small explosives so the fossils would be disturbed as little as possible, workmen blasted away one whole side of the cave, giving easy access, and flatcars hauled off excess dirt. In 1953 the Carnegie Museum of Pittsburgh offered its services in cleaning and identifying specimens. The Museum recorded forty-five species, including snakes, turtles, big-eared bats and a new type of pocket gopher. Most valuable were skeletons of animals that no longer inhabited the region—crocodiles, peccaries, pumas, tapirs, bears and a mastodon.

Valuable as these finds were, they were fragmentary. Paleontologists are always searching and hoping for specimens that will be intact, but in the case of animals, a whole specimen is preserved only when the beast is covered up so quickly after death that it escapes destruction and deterioration.

If entombed in rocks, peat, volcanic ash, tar or amber a specimen may be remarkably preserved. Petrifaction—which occurs when minerals, as a result of chemical changes, replace perishable parts of trees, plant, or skeleton—produces excellent specimens.

Asphalt or tar is one of the most nearly perfect materials for preservation. By studying bones in an old tar seep, often of intermingled species because of the churning effect of upwelling gas and oil, paleontologists can almost reconstruct what happened hundreds of years ago. Perhaps a bison reached too far for a tuft of grass hanging over a pit, or a quail alighted on the surface at dusk and became entangled.

Occasionally paleontologists come upon mummified animals. In a funnel-shaped pit of an extinct volcano crater near Deming, New Mexico, lay a well-preserved ground sloth, mummified by the dry climate. Probably the creature fell into the fumarole and starved to death.

Refrigeration is an equally good preservative. While exploring the banks of the Indigirka River in 1846, a young Russian surveyor named Benkendorf heard a sudden gurgling sound in the water. Then a shapeless, woolly mass bobbed up. "A mammoth!" shouted one of Benkendorf's companions.

With the help of fifty men and some horses, Benkendorf succeeded in pulling the animal ashore, but at that moment the riverbank, undercut by the flood, gave way and the water reclaimed the beast.

Since then both scientists and nonscientists have found mammoths in a standing position under Siberian ice sheets thousands of years old. In subzero caves of the same area stood shaggy ponies frozen stiff.

Removing fossils is often more difficult than locating them, especially if the specimens are embedded in rock. Paleontologists sometimes resort to scaling stone away with a blow torch, but it is a risky operation.

After their field trips, scientists take back to their laboratory plaster of Paris casts, bits of petrified wood, and bones and rocks with plants or animals imprisoned in them. If specimens are to be kept for reference or museum purposes, they must be cleaned, recorded, catalogued and possibly photographed. The paleontologist must also decide on the best means of preservation. Shellac may be applied to surfaces and glue to cracks, but a more up-to-date technique is the application of paraffin.

In this method of preservation, the specimen is preheated and then treated with very hot paraffin, which welds the cracks and prevents flaking or chipping. After the paraffin cools, excess wax is pared off and a blow torch run over the surface. The drawbacks are that paraffin ignites if overheated and a specimen treated with it may explode unless it is thoroughly dry.

Fossils present special problems. Some stones, if heated and then cooled, will crack open and release the plant or animal fossil they enclose, but there is always the danger that the specimen may shatter.

Donald G. MacVicar, Jr., while he was an Amherst senior and chemistry major in 1951, developed a special technique for freeing fossils from limestone. He proved through experimentation that when limestone is heated to approximately 1,800° Centigrade it dissolves into dust. The encased fossil, if phosphate-coated, remains unharmed, and the limestone can be brushed away, leaving the specimen intact. Using this technique on a piece of limestone from a mine in the Belgian Congo, he successfully uncovered the fragile, microscopic remains of a sponge millions of years old.

Paleontologists have a different method for removing fossils from coal balls. To miners and coal dealers these chocolate-brown or muddy grayish balls, varying from golf-ball size to masses weighing several hundred pounds, are a nuisance because they will not burn, but paleontologists prize them. They are pieces of soil and debris which in the Carboniferous or Cretaceous periods became infiltrated with minerals, petrifying the plant remains so that they were not crushed into structureless coal.

The first step in preparing a coal ball for study is to make an exploratory cut with a diamond saw, a circular iron disc with diamond dust embedded in the edge. Using a coarse abrasive such as carborundum, the paleontologist smooths the coarse surface on a grinding lap. Next, a fine abrasive is used. After the specimen has been smoothed, the paleontologist immerses it in dilute acid for several minutes. This procedure etches out the thin layer of mineral matter, leaving plant tissues standing slightly in relief.

The paleontologist places the etched coal ball on a tray of gravel or sand, allows it to dry, and then pours a solution of nitrocellulose, similar to fingernail polish, over it. The nitrocellulose replaces the layer of mineral matter. After it has hardened, the paleontologist can peel the coal ball with the aid of a razor. The peeling brings with it a thin layer of whatever sections of the plant were exposed, and the specimen is then ready for microscopic examination.

A big task confronting paleontologists in the laboratory is the reconstruction of prehistoric animals. Yet scientists, especially those specializing in paleo-zoölogy, are eager to see the animal as it once was. Structural differences—teeth, bones, shape and length—can reveal much about an animal's habits of running, eating and killing prey. Mammals with well-developed canine teeth could eat meat; mammals with low-crowned teeth were probably omnivorous. Animals with modified forelimbs similar to that of moles were equipped to push dirt aside in constructing underground tunnels.

One of the frustrations paleontologists face in reconstruction is that some of the bones which in the field appeared to be prehistoric may, under chemical analysis, turn out to be modern and valueless. There is also the problem of incomplete skeletons. If only a few bones are lacking, the paleontologist usually knows the answer, because most vertebrates are nearly symmetrical. A bone missing on only one side can be supplied by a plaster replica in mirror-image modeled after the other side. Sometimes if the paleontologist has two partial skeletons, he can model parts from one for the other. Ridges, grooves and smooth or rough places on the hard parts tell something about the soft parts of the animal. The general shape and contours can be deduced from the shape and contours of the skeleton.

By adding up all the available details and comparing the specimen with known animals, the scientist can usually determine its class, order and family. By such inferences paleontologists have been able to reconstruct the tusklike, triangular sharks' teeth that tourists sometimes find on the Florida beach about one hundred miles south of Sarasota. Paleontologists believe they belonged to sea-monster sharks that swam in the Gulf of Mexico millions of years ago.

One type, the Giant Carcharodon shark, perhaps a hundred and fifty feet long, had from six to eight rows of teeth, with forty or more in each row. When a tooth almost as big as the palm of a human hand was damaged or lost, one from the reserve row worked forward to take its place. There is a restoration of the jaws of the Carcharodon shark in the American Museum of Natural History in New York City. If a man should stand inside the lower teeth, his entire height would be less than half of the opened jaws.

Paleontologists are more confident about their reconstructions of skeletons than of an ancient animal's surface features—its color, length of hair and shape of ears. For all they know, horses of the past may have been striped like zebras.

If reconstructed plants or animals are to be used for museum displays, paleontologists assemble collections of them according to their region and time period, which requires fitting together all possible clues as to climate, terrain and contemporary plants and animals. A re-creation of the plant and animal life in forested areas of ancient Germany was greatly facilitated by the discovery of insects and leaves preserved in amber in the Baltic Sea region.

The ants, flies, mosquitoes and spiders, and occasionally leaves, petals and bird feathers, had been imprisoned in resin as it oozed from a tree or lay on the ground in a sticky condition. Later, the resin had solidified, making fossils of the objects, and much of it was washed into the sea.

Through their research paleontologists have traced progressive changes from primitive types to present-day animals. Over a time interval of perhaps sixty million years, the horse changed from a four-toed, flat-footed animal only slightly larger than a fox to the animal it now is. Living coelacanths dredged up from the sea may, according to some paleontologists, be the link between fish in the sea and vertebrates on the land.

In a former glacial bog in Wyoming, students from Harvard and the University of Wyoming found an elk, a deer, a wolf and a large, extinct bison which weighed seven hundred pounds and stood over eleven feet tall. Stone knives lying in the marsh indicated

COELACANTH

that the bison was killed by men more than twelve thousand years ago.

In Cherokee Cave under the heart of the City of St. Louis, Missouri, scientists from the American Museum of Natural History in New York found thousands of bones and skulls of peccaries that had inhabited the cave. Although fierce-looking, these piglike animals apparently subsisted on vegetation, uprooting plants with their tusks.

From fossils, paleontologists can deduce the effects of climate and natural catastrophes on life in a given region. The variety of species in the Cumberland Cave attest to radical changes in climate. Paleontologists agree that over the centuries bones worked down through the crevices. When advancing glaciers brought Arctic conditions, minks, martens and mastodons roamed the frigid Cumberland. The retreat of the ice front forced these animals to seek cooler climes. They were replaced by temperate-zone animals—skunks, muskrats, beaver, and deer; but increasing warmth and humidity caused these, in turn, to disappear, to be followed by such semi-tropical beasts as peccaries, snakes and tigers. Then decreasing humidity brought prairie animals—coyotes, pumas and rabbits.

The climatic conditions that preserved the mastodons in ice are less clear. The number of skeletons unearthed indicate that millions of beasts once flourished in regions now bitterly cold. How did animals of a temperate climate become entrapped in a mile-thick ice sheet? What sequence of events preserved them?

Since it is a known fact that ivory tusks as well as animal flesh change structure very rapidly if exposed to air at normal temperatures, the great ice sheet which entombed mastodons, mammoths, giant beavers and saber-toothed tigers in perfect condition must have descended abruptly, probably as the result of some violent wrenching of the earth's crust. One paleontological explanation is that the animals were killed by deep snowfalls and buried in freezing mud, following a sudden weather change caused by some distant volcanic holocaust. Some theorize that the brutes fell through the thin ice into glaciers.

Fossils sometimes reveal facts on the geography of the past, as well as climate. Because bones of extinct bears, hyenas, bison and tigers found underground in England are identical with those found in France, Belgium and Germany, paleontologists believe that a bridge of land once connected the British Isles to the European continent.

From the skeletons of our long-dead human ancestors, paleontologists can study their size, tell what diseases afflicted them and reveal some of their habits. The methods of dating and the system of nomenclature used for various stages of man's development cannot be dealt with in a chapter of this length.

Although paleontologists study the past, much of the information gained solves problems of the present. Petroleum companies frequently rely on paleontologists to help in locating oil. Fossils which come up in drill cores give the paleontologist a good idea of when the rock was formed, and from its age he can tell whether it is likely to yield petroleum. Proximity to gold-bearing formations can also be determined by the age of fossils in overlying sedimentary rocks.

With their knowledge of life of the past, paleontologists hold keys that may unlock vast stores of underground treasures. There are tremendous gaps in our information—whole ages about which almost nothing is known. There are still unanswered questions as to how plants and animals fit into the general stream of evolution. Until the answers are found, paleontologists will continue to dig up their rocks, bones, fossils and shells that reveal the secrets of the book of Earth.

16

Scientific Treasure Hunters

When archaeologists pry, probe, map and measure, the treasures they reclaim may be worth very little in terms of money but are extremely valuable because of what they reveal. Jewels, weapons, tools and bits of broken pottery all have a tale to tell about what people of the past made, did, said and thought. From a study of these products of human workmanship, known as artifacts, archaeologists can reconstruct the story of man and his life. Historians usually concentrate on kings, cardinals and politicians, but archaeologists are interested in the everyday lives of the John and Mary Does.

Archaeologists choose a site for an expedition because they have reason to believe that in the past city dwellers or a hunting or agricultural group lived there, and they are seeking answers to specific questions about what happened in the region at a particular time. How did the people make a living? What did they do for entertainment? What were their religious beliefs? Did they write, paint and make music?

Incentives for the search may be provided by science, history, maps or mere chance. Archaeologists are great lovers of maps. Poring over outmoded ones, they may find an ancient city that left no visible trace. Literary or historical accounts may excite their curiosity about an ancient people. As a small boy growing up in Germany, Heinrich Schliemann was fascinated with stories about the wars between Greece and Troy. On what plains was the long war fought to win the beautiful Helen? Where was Priam's palace and the gate through which the unwary Trojans dragged the wooden horse? Schliemann, almost penniless as a boy, made a fortune in the indigo trade and devoted it to excavating the city of his dreams.

Sometimes such natural forces as wind or water erosion uncover clues for exploring archaeologists. The erosive action of the Danube River betrayed evidence of long-buried settlements; and when exceptional droughts lowered the level of Lake Zurich, the remains of villages of Lake Dwellers lay exposed.

Men who disturb the soil with tools or machinery sometimes make archaeological finds by accident. After an English farmer in Norfolk ploughed up some gold ornaments and coins, archaeologists examined the field and found more items dating back to about the time of the birth of Jesus.

During World War II, when fire and bombs leveled much of the city of London, workmen found signs of buried walls beneath the rubble of bomb-blasted buildings. Archaeologists, digging systematically, unearthed blockhouses, roads and chariot ways, reminders of Roman occupation about 70 to 90 A.D. Alert to further possibilities, archaeologists founded the Roman and Medieval London Excavation Council. In 1954 on a site cleared for the erection of a large building, members of the Council found a Roman head carved of stone. Later efforts of the excavators were rewarded by the discovery of an ancient pagan temple built to honor Mithras, the bull slayer and god of light. Mithraism had originated in Persia. The excavation roused so much popular interest that the owner of the site promised to dismantle the remains carefully and re-erect the temple in the forecourt of his new building.

Scientific hunches sometimes lead to the location of ancient sites. When looking for the Biblical city of Gibeon, pillaged by Nebuchadnezzar, archaeologist James B. Pritchard selected his digging site on the theory that water would have been an important factor in the city's location, and that Gibeon must have been built on the brow of a hill near a spring. Excavation confirmed his reasoning.

For exploring possible sites in regions normally almost inaccessible, aerial reconnaissance is a valuable tool. When intelligently applied it also adds to our knowledge of areas already investigated.

Stone buildings which collapsed and were covered over by soil centuries ago leave permanent traces on the surface of the land. Buried walls, because they drain off moisture, tend to stunt the growth of plants above them. On the other hand, graves, storage pits, and tunnels give roots additional room and moisture and permit more luxurious crops. To a person walking over the pits, tunnels or graves the markings may not be noticeable, but to an archaeologist soaring above them in a plane the patterns of vegetation show with amazing accuracy the presence of ancient cities, military camps and burial grounds.

Aerial photos showed clearly the demarcation of streets of an old Roman town near Silchester, England, which had been buried for fifteen hundred years beneath a crisscross of hedges and modern highways. Among the most significant discoveries made by aerial observation was Woodhenge, a monument of the same general type as Stonehenge, only made of wood.

There is some element of luck in digging, but a large-scale archaeological expedition reduces the risk by purposeful surface reconnaissance before making the final selection of a site. The archaeologist studies physical, topographic and geologic maps of a region, and if there is no detailed map of the area, he makes one. He consults botanical and geological sources on the nature of forests and grasslands of the past.

In small settlements or in open country, natives or shepherds can often lead an archaeologist to places where relics can be found. Whether in a jeep or on foot the archaeologist watches for clues. Fragments of pottery in a cellar excavation or ancient bricks still used by peasants may denote the presence of a buried city. Mounds may give away the presence of an ancient village. Middle East natives never bothered to remove the remains of a previous settlement, but simply built on top of it. Because decomposition of organic substances increases the proportion of minerals, soil analysis of a region can give hints of prior settlement.

Sometimes archaeologists make seismic or electrical resistivity tests, much as geophysicists or mining geologists do when pros-

159

pecting, since it is a known fact that arable land contains more water than the stones of ancient buildings. By making systematic measures of resistivity, it is possible to determine where the subsoil conceals remnants of buildings or old, filled-in excavations. Although they are not completely foolproof, electrical resistivity tests have often shown exactly where to dig.

If a large-scale expedition is planned, its sponsors may send out a preliminary survey party to make sure that the expense of a full-scale expedition will be warranted. Walter Fairservis, Jr., who studied at the Oriental Institute of the University of Chicago, and Bill Davidson, a dramatist but also an archaeologist, headed such an expedition to Afghanistan in 1949. In this brooding, forbidden, almost unknown land, the archaeologists knew they should find answers about life in the days of Ghengis Khan, the Asiatic conqueror who swept through the land with his destructive horde of followers.

The Fairservis-Davidson expedition, sponsored by the American Museum of Natural History, made test digs in cities where nothing but jackals and vultures had lived for centuries. Once the expedition almost lost its equipment in a flooded river. For four grueling days the men had to buck searing winds on the Desert of Death. Only half alive, they staggered into the ruins of a ghost city abandoned by the Moslems when its water supply dried up in the sixteenth century.

Although the mission had at times hovered on the brink of disaster, Fairservis and Davidson reported that Afghanistan was an archaeological gold mine and recommended further exploration. Their experiences roused such popular interest that when the expedition returned to Afghanistan, *Collier*'s magazine sent reporters to record the activities and discoveries in words and pictures.

As soon as a specific site has been selected, archaeologists learn everything possible about the land they intend to explore and the customs of its people. They saturate themselves with facts about the period or periods of history they expect to find represented.

Equipping a big expedition takes large sums of money. In many countries the government subsidizes them, but in the United States museums, universities, scientific organizations and foundations assume the responsibility. If going to a remote, isolated spot, the archaeologists must assemble hundreds of items from jeeps, generators and tools for excavation to medical supplies and canned goods.

There are always many technical details such as obtaining passports, getting permission to dig at selected sites, arranging for shipment of supplies. Making up a staff is a formidable task, since expeditions need men who not only have the requisite scientific skills but also can adapt to unusual living conditions. Besides archaeologists, a large expedition may include an architect, an engineer, a photographer, a linguist and other specialists. On smaller expeditions one individual may serve in several capacities.

At the selected site archaeologists may first need to clear away underbrush. The photographer takes a picture of the unexcavated location and a surveyor fixes a base line and assigns a serial number. The site is then divided into grids with metal or wooden pegs at every intersection point.

At any site there is likely to be an enormous amount of digging. Local residents usually assist in this work, but they must be carefully instructed. The spade of the amateur can destroy the evidence being sought and make the past unreadable. Early archaeologists, more treasure hunters than scientists, attacked their sites helter-skelter and thus unwittingly ruined valuable artifacts. Today, although archaeologists know that some destruction is inevitable, they try to keep it to a minimum. They are much more likely to wield a grapefruit knife than a spade. One archaeologist, removing a fragile object with the aid of a penknife and a water color brush, was so engrossed that he was unaware of any spectators until a native remarked, "That be a watchmaker's job."

The extraction of delicate objects demands patience, skill and knowledge of methods. To speed up the location of metal objects, some archaeologists use electromagnetic detectors of the type employed during World War II for mine disposal. Unfortunately the detectors cannot distinguish between a valuable artifact such as a weapon and a nail or an old tin can.

To remove thin metal objects, the archaeologist brushes or blows

161

as much soil away as possible. Then he may ladle hot wax over and around the object and cover it with a piece of muslin dipped in wax. He next digs away from under the object until it is supported on a thin column of earth and can be tilted over onto a padded board. The earth is removed from the under side and more wax and muslin are applied so that the object can be transported.

Archaeologists do a great deal of stratigraphical, or layer, analysis. Within each grid the soil is peeled off carefully layer by layer and sieved or sifted so nothing is overlooked. Layers of decayed vegetation laid down by nature alternate with layers of ashes left behind by fires of primitive men. Sometimes in mounds containing cities, workmen cut away a whole side to make the layers visible.

It is important that diggers recognize changes in strata revealed by color and content because each layer usually represents a completely different civilization. Mixture of artifacts from two layers could make the research meaningless.

Archaeologists assume that the artifacts in the bottom layer are oldest, perhaps reaching back to the Stone Age. By careful study of successive strata, archaeologists can trace the evolution of tools, pottery, weapons, basketry and shelters. Much can be deduced from study of items missing in one layer but appearing in the next.

It is the excitement of coming upon finds that relieves the monotony of digging. The archaeologist never knows what his trowel will turn up next. Even the discovery of a simple cup can set off a series of questions. Whose hands held it? Was it an everyday cup or a banquet one? What was served in it?

As they dig, archaeologists fit together some pieces of the puzzle. Old seeds of wheat bear witness to farming; artifacts in graves indicate belief in a future life.

The rediscovery of a lost city is one of the most fascinating of archaeological adventures. Sometimes a great city was burnt and was never repeopled. Sometimes it was abandoned because water became inadequate or some great natural disaster overtook it. Pompeii, inundated by volcanic ash, emerged almost intact from the dust and ashes as if time had stood still waiting to give archaeologists a glimpse of ancient modes of life.

In 1961 archaeologists from a Cornell-Harvard University expedition unearthed the shopping center at Sardis, Asia Minor, which once lured bargain-hunting Lydians. Digging down through cobblestones, archaeologists found a shopping street some fifty feet wide, paved with marble and flanked by colonnades that sheltered ancient shoppers from sun or rain. Adjacent to the shopping center the scientists uncovered a Roman gymnasium, fragments of which bore inscriptions indicating a construction date of 211 or 212 A.D. From their findings archaeologists concluded that the shopping street probably originated in the time of the fabulously rich Croesus, King of Lydia. Disaster had struck when the Persians overran the city, and at a still later date Byzantine engineers had overlaid the marble street with cobblestones.

The archaeological quest often centers on the lives of herdsmen and farmers rather than city dwellers. In any case, the archaeologist seeks what the man left behind that reveals what he did and what he believed.

Tombs may reveal fascinating artifacts. Many ancient peoples, believing that in life beyond the grave the departed one would need what he had used on earth, buried innumerable everyday objects. Archaeologists were eager to locate and open Etruscan tombs in Italy because little was known about the Etruscans, who controlled northern and central Italy twenty-five centuries ago.

The first tombs opened abounded in artifacts which testified to a powerful, wealthy, luxury-loving, talented, highly civilized people. To answer questions about Etruscan religion, trade, art, government, archaeologists needed further evidence from the Tombs of Gold, as they began calling them. Archaeologists had no trouble locating them, but frequently found after long hours of strenuous digging that the tombs had already been raided. Both ancient and modern grave robbers had found a ready market for Etruscan jewels, art and pottery.

Italian Signor Carlo Lerici, an engineer and amateur archaeologist, deplored the difficult, time-consuming and expensive excavations of tombs which so often ended in disappointment. If only a system could be devised whereby an archaeologist could see inside

163

a tomb, he thought, he could then determine whether it would repay the effort of excavation.

In 1957 Lerici introduced a tomb-probing technique combining electrical resistivity and photography. By electronic echo sounders he located the approximate center of the tomb. Then, with a portable drill, he bored a hole just large enough to accommodate a tube enclosing a tiny Minox camera and a synchronized flash. Through a control device above the ground, he could activate and rotate the camera so it took pictures of the interior from various angles, and the photographs revealed whether the tomb contained artifacts or had been despoiled.

But Lerici still regretted the delay caused by developing and printing films. Working with his associates at the Lerici Foundation of the Milan Polytechnic Institute, he devised a periscopic tube which enabled him to cover his head with a black cloth and peer inside a tomb. The illumination from a light in the tube permitted him to appraise the buried artifacts. If he wished, he could take photographs. In one ten-week period, Lerici examined one hundred and twenty tombs. All except ten were already barren or worthless because of destruction due to dampness or aftereffects of earthquakes, but the coins, votive lamps, bronze statues and other objects from the tombs that were opened revealed much about Etruscan art, religion and recreation. Lerici and Prof. Renato Bartoccini, director of Rome's National Museum of Etruscan Art, using the Lerici technique for location, found an amazing collection of jewelry, weapons and fine ceramics in the Olympiad Tomb. The pottery had the earmarks of Greek craftsmanship, indicating that the Etruscans traded with foreigners, but they were also skilled craftsmen in their own right.

Archaeologists often spend as much time recording and evaluating items as they do digging them up. Most expeditions keep two sets of day-to-day sheets. One records operations in progress; men employed; visitors, if any; levels dug into; details on weather; jobs completed and antiquities found. The second sheet gives a minute description of the progress made in each separate operation.

Every object excavated, be it only a bead, is recorded with date

164

of discovery and stratigraphic position. If the find is a piece of pottery, it may be measured, described as to shape, color, texture and design, and analyzed as to structure. Its relation to the other objects, to the place in which it was found—in other words, its context—must be carefully noted.

Slipshod, hasty recording can make the work of excavation almost useless. Later, archaeologists working in the museum or laboratory to get an over-all picture of life in a given area will want to know if the pot was found near a fireplace, whether other objects lay around it, whether it was close to a source of water, whether there were remains of bones and charcoal nearby. If there were bones, they want to know what kinds of animals were indicated. If the pot was in a house, they are interested in what kind of timbers had been used.

Photography is extremely important in recording. In one exposure, a camera can capture what it would take pages of notes to describe. Frequently a photographer takes pictures that will serve as a chart for reconstruction. With a pattern to go by, archaeologists can take up mosaic floors and reassemble them in a far-distant museum.

Archaeological research requires unusual perseverance. Sensational finds are not achieved by a few strokes of a pick. A miscalculation in clues may lead to the futile removal of tons of earth, and archaeologists may dig for months, or even years, without uncovering any really significant artifacts. This was the case with the party led by the English archaeologist Howard Carter working in the Valley of the Kings near Luxor, Egypt. Discouraged after ten years of fruitless research, Carter and his patron, Lord Carnarvon, in the autumn of 1922, decided to leave the region.

On the morning of November 26, Carter and several men in the expedition decided to make one last, despairing effort. After clearing a deep hole, the diggers uncovered a sealed doorway. Making a breach in the upper left hand corner, Carter inserted a candle and peered in. Everywhere he looked he saw the glint of gold.

Carter had found the Tomb of Tutankhamen, an Egyptian king who had reigned over Egypt in the fourteenth century B.C. It took several years to bring out the trove of amulets, statues, silver trumpets, furniture inlaid with gold, jars of perfume, caskets of jewelry and golden effigies of the king. As in any other expedition, the objects, which gave a remarkable insight into the life of the period, had to be recorded and cleaned.

GOLD AMULET FROM TUTANKHAMEN'S TOMB

Golden objects are usually recovered in good condition, but silver ones may be tarnished and bronze ones stained with green. To care for pottery, most large expeditions have sheds with washing equipment consisting of trays of various sizes, drying mats, washing bowls, nail brushes, soft paint or pottery brushes. Experts determine what chemicals will do the best job of restoration.

In dry climates, artifacts are likely to be in good condition; but in hot, moist areas, insects, humidity and soil acidity often have caused almost total destruction. Archaeologists are often disappointed to find artifacts that are only fragmentary, because wood cracks, leather loses its suppleness, textiles rot, and a piece of pottery saturated with underground moisture will disintegrate if exposed too quickly to sunlight.

Archaeologists often attempt to reconstruct an artifact through making careful measurements, studying imprints it has made in the soil and comparing it with similar finds. Their skill has resulted in fine restorations of a wide variety of things, including harps, sledges, chariots and Viking ships.

The digging, recording, restoring, sorting, and packing may be carried on in far-away, exotic-sounding places, but life at "the dig" is likely to be rather primitive. If the expedition is a large one working over a long period of time in reasonably civilized areas, archaeologists may enjoy ordinary comforts. But more often than not the archaeologist lives in a tent with light produced by a lamp and heat by a charcoal brazier.

During the summer of 1961, eighteen university students shared thatched huts of Mayan Indians in Guatemala. They ate corn tortillas and little else. Archaeologists at one site in Turkey had trouble with donkeys and sheep invading the camp, and at night howling jackals disturbed their sleep.

In the past, some natives of the regions being excavated, misunderstanding the goals of archaeologists, often hampered or even attacked parties doing research in their country. Efforts made by archaeologists today to avoid violations of native customs have diminished hostility. But as recently as 1938, Moslem bandits, angered by the presence of Hindu archaeologists in the Indian province of Sind, attacked the party, wounding three of the workmen and killing the Hindu archaeologist N. G. Majumdar, leader of the expedition.

Legal details may also cause complications. Archaeologist Robert J. Braidwood, associated with the Oriental Institute of the University of Chicago, once had a costly ten-day delay at Beirut, Lebanon, getting clearance for cars needed by the expedition. Before the final documentation was accomplished, a cloudburst caved in the roof of the police department office, and locating the proper file took the officials four days longer.

At such times archaeologists are likely to assert that never again will they go forth on another expedition. But back in the laboratory the archaeologist tends to forget the monotonous hours of digging, the deep disappointments, the delays and the false trails. Handling some rare specimen he remembers the sudden surprise, the excitement of unearthing a dagger, a clay tablet or a jewel case, although not one of the treasures was his to keep. He can almost feel the warm sun on his back. With nostalgia he thinks of the close companionship of men welded together by a common purpose. He is plagued by such unanswered questions as Where did the Sumerians come from? or Who built the idols on Easter Island?

He knows that answers to these and other questions lie buried in Peru, Afghanistan, Lebanon, or some South Sea island. So once more the archaeologist resolves to go forth to unearth every shred of information that might deepen his understanding of the past. His skill, patience, courage and endurance will almost certainly provide new clues to the when, where and how of lost civilizations.

17

Drowned Cities, Ships and Relics

Port Royal, Jamaica, once the center of the West Indian slave trade, had the reputation of being the most wicked city in the world. Many refugees from justice lived there. Buccaneers used the hustling port as home base for their piracy. On June 17, 1692, a violent earthquake jolted the city. Fort James and Fort Carlisle, located near the harbor, sank into the sea, as did houses for several blocks inland. Tidal waves followed. Two thousand persons lost their lives. Port Royal, two-thirds destroyed, never regained its former position and became a sleepy fishing village.

Tales of Port Royal and other sunken cities, as well as of ships lost at sea, have been the basis for dreams of marble halls and galleons with gold in their hold. Archaeologists have always thought the likelihood of recovering such prizes slight, but they have long entertained the idea of the sea as a vast museum. The big questions were how buried cities or wrecks of ancient ships could be located and how artifacts could be salvaged. Until the advent of divers with aqualungs, archaeologists had to rely mainly on written reports to locate vanished cities or sunken ships.

On record in a museum in Tunis was an account of the sinking of a large Greek ship that had blown off its course in a storm during the days of the Roman Empire. The ship had gone down off the African coast near the site of the ancient city of Carthage. In 1948 the oceanographer Captain Jacques Cousteau, interested in the possibility of using aqualung equipment for submarine archaeology, consulted the Mahdia records hoping to salvage the wreck.

One attempt had already been made years earlier to bring up the ship's cargo. Cousteau thought further salvage operations might be fruitful because the ship had presumably been carrying systematically gathered loot of the Roman dictator Lucius Cornelius Sulla, who had sacked Athens in 86 B.C. Unfortunately, landmarks had changed since the site had been described in the museum entry, and Cousteau could not at first locate the wreckage. Divers did eventually find the remains of the ship, but by then time and funds had run out. Cousteau and his crew had only a collection of marble columns to show for their efforts.

During the nineteen fifties skin diving and the use of aqualungs became more widespread and reports of underseas artifacts increased. One diver in the vicinity of the Blue Grotto on the Isle of Capri found the remains of steps and other parts of a man-made structure thought to have been used by the Roman Emperor Tiberius when he went bathing. Another diver announced that in Lake Titicaca in the Bolivian Andes he had discovered the cast-offs of a pre-Inca city. After photographs taken by a Bolivian archaeologist substantiated the claim, divers and scientists brought up stone implements and other artifacts which told much about the Incas who had lived on the lakeshore centuries ago.

Occasionally fishermen help archaeologists locate likely sites. When Italian Marquis Piero Nicola Gargallo inquired into the source of Etruscan-looking objects sold to tourists by Tyrrhenian fishermen, they offered to lead him to the reef where they had fished them up. With an aqualung strapped on his back, Gargallo explored the reef thoroughly. About a mile off the Tyrrhenian coast he found weed-grown chunks of cut marble and something that looked like a street or pier. Gargallo had found the ancient Etruscan seaport of Pyrgi.

Inadvertently a diver set off the most extended project yet attempted in the field of submarine archaeology. Frederic Dumas, a co-partner of Cousteau's in aqualung research, visited a commercial diver, Christianini, hospitalized as the result of staying down too long under water. Christianini referred to the abundance of lobsters off the coast at Marseilles, France. What puzzled him, he told Dumas, was the presence of a large number of big jars strewn along the floor of the lobster banks. Dumas didn't think much about the jars until Christianini mentioned a mound on the ocean floor near Grand Congloué, the last island to the east in a chain of barren, jagged rocks opposite the city of Marseilles.

Dumas passed this information along to Cousteau, who was much excited by the possibility that the mound concealed an ancient wreck. If the ship or its cargo could be salvaged, archaeologists would have new clues to shipbuilding and commerce of the past. Objects carried in the vessels would also explain much about everyday life in ancient times. Preliminary exploration convinced Cousteau and Dumas that the site was worth exploring.

From the Ministry of Education and the French Navy, Cousteau secured funds to convert the *Calypso* to archaeological purposes and to hire skilled divers. As archaeological consultants he engaged Ferdinand Lallemand and Fernard Benoît, head of the Marseilles Archeological Museum. Cousteau had in his favor experience gained during archaeological research carried out off the coast of Tunis. He now had trained divers to draw upon and he had learned a great deal about suitable techniques for reclaiming submarine treasures.

In 1952 the *Calypso* took up a position off the bleak coast of Grand Congloué, which looked much like a stone iceberg chewed by wind and waves into fantastic shapes. Dumas made the first dive. When he came up emptyhanded, Benoît was disappointed. Cousteau then went down, but found only one amphora, a graceful two-handled earthenware jar used by ancient peoples for storage of wine, water, oil or grain. Cargo ships of Phoenicia, Greece, Carthage and Rome had carried thousands of these in racks in holds. Pointed at the bottom, they could, when being used on land, stand upright in soft soil.

Cousteau was about to returned to the *Calypso* when he noticed a pile of dishes. He grabbed a cup and made a slow upward ascent.

When Cousteau surfaced, Benoît, who had been waiting in a

launch shouted, "Campanian!" He went on to explain that modern archaeologists prize this black dinnerware.

After that, divers undertook a day after day search for objects of interest as well as for the ship which must have transported them. Usually two divers went down together for a period no longer than seventeen minutes. Breathing compressed air which automatically pressurized them, they could descend to two hundred feet. At the end of the allotted period, watchers on board fired two rounds of ammunition into the water, which set up vibrations that served as signals to the aqualunged men. On their way up, divers paused at the thirty-foot mark, indicated on the air lift pipe, for eight minutes, then again at ten feet for three minutes, to allow for decompression. After a rest period, they repeated their descent, averaging from three to five dives per day.

At first the divers found many amphorae, but not much else. A few of the jars were still sealed, but most had been opened and had become repositories for sand, silt, shells and blinking octopuses. After a while, divers located the ship which they believed to be a Roman merchantman with lead sheathing, but so much mud lay on top of it that they couldn't tell the stern from the bow.

To clear thick, deep mud off the ship and artifacts, Cousteau and his crew devised high-pressure air lines which swept the wreck vacuum cleaner fashion, but also raised clouds of bubbly black water which obscured the vision of the divers.

A suction pipe sniffed up mud in which lay buried bronze hooks, copper nails, knives, and bronze finger rings. Hanging from a long boom, the pipe, when loaded, would spit out water and debris into a filtering basket anchored on the coastline of Grand Congloué. Archaeologists kept watch and retrieved artifacts from the basket. Excess mud and water drained back into the sea.

On days when nothing appeared except amphorae brought up by hand in seemingly endless succession, archaeologists became discouraged. But divers could not get into the hold until they cleared the jars out. To relieve the monotony of toiling in the cold, dim water, they sometimes played tricks on the archaeologists stationed at the filter baskets waiting for treasures. Once the divers sent up a small octopus through the suction pipe, another time coins. Lallemand, who had previously expressed to the divers the hope that there would be coins which would reveal the basis of a monetary system, seized them eagerly. When he had washed the mud off, he saw the five-franc pieces were dated 1950.

As weeks passed into months, divers brought up a lead anchor, elegant black dishes with red decorations, and hundreds of amphorae. Benoît and Lallemand, assisted by off-duty divers, cleaned, sorted, classified, recorded and assessed every item, whether splinters of wood or cargo. Fitting details together, the archaeologists agreed that the Roman merchantman must have been equipped with sails, since it was too large to be propelled by oars. They estimated the date of building to be between 205–230 B.C., which meant that the ship had lain for centuries undisturbed by groping hands.

The amphorae aboard seemed to indicate that the vessel had sailed with a cargo loaded on the Greek Island of Delos. At what is now Naples it had probably sold Greek wine and taken on dinnerware. At Rome it stocked wine for customers in Marseilles. Almost in sight of port, the ship had foundered.

Cousteau and the archaeologists became anxious as their finances dwindled and finds seemed relatively insignificant. In November, 1952, a buoy floated out of position and Jean Pierre Servanti, a personable young diver of whom Cousteau had become very fond, volunteered to go down and inspect the chain. Something went wrong and the dive ended in death for Servanti.

Feeling he had no right to risk lives, no matter how valuable the research might be, Cousteau wanted to terminate the project, but scientists urged him to continue. So did a friend of Servanti's, who the day after the tragedy sent a telegram offering his services as a replacement. Deeply touched, Cousteau decided to go ahead.

Realizing that the research would extend over many months, possibly years, Cousteau and his crew, with some assistance from the French navy, built on the shores of Grand Congloué a platform for emergency equipment to power the underwater suction pipes. On the cliff above the platform, they erected a tin house with a kitchen, dining room, and beds for eight people.

Cousteau, grateful for the dedication of his divers over a period of months, wanted to show appreciation. For New Year's Eve he invited the divers and guests from Marseilles to a party in the tin shack. At midnight after a meal served on dishes fished up from the sea, and an evening of hilarity, diver Pierre Labat called out, "Who will bring up the first amphora of 1953?" The divers immediately donned aqualungs.

The ones brought up that night were the first of an unending succession of amphorae during 1953. Many had the initials SES and trident symbols on them. Benoît set forth on a quest for information on the merchant who might have shipped them. Searching genealogies in Italy, he found there had been a prominent Roman clan named Sestius. Could the SES stand for Sestius? Reading further Benoît learned that Marcus Sestius, a noted merchant shipowner, had gone to the Greek island of Delos to set up a shipping business.

Determined to unravel the archaeological mystery, Benoît went to Delos. In the ruins of a house some thought had once belonged to a family named Sestius, he saw tiles with the same trident markings as the amphorae. Black volcanic pebbles in the courtyard matched pebbles found in the wreck which had baffled scientists because they were unlike those in the vicinity where the ship had gone down.

Archaeological explanations such as this intrigued Cousteau, but he was concerned over the time wasted because divers were not trained in archaeology. Sometimes they brought up items which added nothing of importance to the collections. Often when archaeologists, interested in context, wanted exact descriptions of relationships to each other or to the ship, divers answered eloquently but vaguely.

Cousteau needed archaeologists who could use aqualungs, but had no success in finding them. The next best solution, he thought, would be to develop underwater television so an archaeologist could remain on shipboard and yet direct operations by asking for close observations of a specific object or area.

The British Thomson-Houston Company offered the use of TV cameras, cables and monitors. Dr. Pierre Dratz, of the National Center for Scientific Research, built a special lens and André Laban, a young engineer, helped Cousteau construct a watertight camera caisson flanked by flood lights. In the spring of 1953 the television camera was lowered into the sea.

A loudspeaker encased in a container and connected with a surface microphone permitted archaeologists to give instructions to divers. If the diver wanted the archaeologists to examine a find he could push the television to it. A large porthole at the back of the container allowed him to watch on a small screen a reduced copy of the image appearing on shipboard so he could check what was being transmitted. Buoyed cables connected the TV to the ship. Archaeologists were disheartened when the first picture revealed little except a tired-looking fish and a desolate expanse of mud. Divers felt self-conscious at being televised.

Later, Cousteau and others worked out improvements which resulted in satisfactory pictures. Lallemand and Benoît were enthusiastic. They pointed out to Cousteau that they could see as much as if they went below themselves; but freed from the mechanism of exploration, they could think clearly and direct investigations intelligently. Divers soon saw the advantage of simultaneous viewing for coordinating instructions and saving time. Underwater television also added to their feeling of security. If anything went wrong, friends watching on board could send help immediately.

After *Calypso* divers got past the amphorae which had blocked their entry into the ship, they found other varieties of jars, bowls with elaborate ornamentation, and saucers covered with black varnish and stamped with palm leaves and rosettes. There were objects of mortar, marble statues and a portable earthenware stove. The long-drawn-out exploration had depleted Cousteau's funds, but just when he thought he would have to discontinue the research, the Marseilles Chamber of Commerce and the United States' National Geographic Society came to the rescue.

Another problem arose when Cousteau needed the *Calypso* to carry out a mission to locate underseas oil. Finally he engaged the *Espadon,* formerly a fishing vessel, to hover over the site and serve as a floating base for the small crew of divers who would continue work on the project.

By 1957 hundreds of artifacts had been transferred from the floor of the Mediterranean to the Museum in Marseilles, where Benoît cleaned, classified, arranged and displayed them. From the finds, Benoît and Lallemand had drawn many deductions about the craftsmanship of the men who had made the ship and the items in its cargo. Benoît published the data. For the benefit of submarine archaeologists, he provided sketches of the site off Grand Congloué and also described the techniques of submarine archaeology.

Cousteau's experimentation encouraged archaeologists to look beneath the sea. Among these was Edwin A. Link, inventor of the Link Trainer for pilots, but also an amateur archaeologist. Wouldn't it be possible, he asked himself, to apply aqualung and television techniques to research on the sunken city of Port Royal? Whatever he found would be truly indicative of the times, since the city had lain undisturbed by picks or trowels. His preliminary explorations in 1956 promised so much that Link succeeded in getting backing from the Institute of Jamaica, the National Geographic Society and the Smithsonian Institution. Three years later, with the luxurious, specially-equipped *Sea Diver,* he returned to the harbor at Port Royal.

The first vessel to be designed exclusively for underwater archaeology, the *Sea Diver* had heavy-duty jetting hose, sturdy air compressors for filling divers' tanks quickly, radar and echo sounders. Underwater ports provided excellent opportunities for observation. A diving chamber near the stern was located nearly flush with the surface of the water. A lower door, which opened downward, formed a ladder.

Link was armed with an old map of the section of the city destroyed which indicated its approximate location, but the water was so murky and the city so buried by silt that he had to resort to sonar survey and use of underwater metal detectors. Divers reported

176

what appeared to be warehouses, ship supply stores and kitchens of ordinary dwellings, and soon began bringing up pots and dishes.

For advice on the dating and interpretation of artifacts, Link had the help of Mandel Peterson, marine archaeologist from the Smithsonian Institution. Peterson thought the pewter spoons, copper lanterns and tortoise-shell combs were probably products of the sixteen nineties, when Port Royal had been a gay, pleasure-loving city, but a cannon dated back to Columbus's time.

One of the most interesting finds was a watch with silver Roman numerals still distinctly visible. The watch had been under a layer of coral, which probably accounted for the cleanliness of the brass gears. The hands were missing, but an X-ray photograph revealed faint traces of them. They pointed to seventeen minutes before twelve—the exact moment of the quake that resulted in death and disaster for Port Royal.

Link's divers brought up hundreds of artifacts from the sea; yet at the end of the second year the possibilities were far from exhausted. Further research would have given added answers, but Link did not feel justified in spending more money and time when artifacts already rescued gave a pretty clear picture of life in Port Royal of 1692.

In recent years it has become increasingly evident that aqualungs can be as useful to archaeologists as a trowel or spade. Submarine archaeology, although it has drawbacks, also has some advantages over land archaeology.

Water is often destructive, but it can also preserve. Pottery pieces in water, larger than those on land because they have escaped trampling, reveal more about their original shape, size and decorations. Underwater objects are protected from weather and the greedy hands that have looted ships and cities.

Lakes, inland pools and deep wells (cenotes) sometimes yield more artifacts per square foot than land areas. Because some cenotes in Central America, regarded as sacred by Mayans, contain a variety of objects offered to appease the gods, several recent expeditions in Central America, although primarily land expeditions, included divers among their staffs. In such wells, objects are concentrated because they have sunk to the bottom, and no layer by layer analysis is involved.

During the mid-nineteen fifties, a National Geographic Society-Tulane University team of archaeologists, surveyors, divers and artisans explored the remains of Dzibilchaltun in Yucatan. Research showed that in its day the metropolis, possibly the largest and longest-inhabited city of ancient America, must have had an impressive central area with pyramided temples, a palace, and buildings of vaulted stone. After the structures collapsed, builders of highways and haciendas had ravaged Dzibilchaltun. But mounds of earth and a deep well which had been the main source of the city's water supply guarded their treasures.

Divers employed by that expedition brought up such valuable artifacts that in the summer of 1957 the National Geographic Society sent some of its staff members to participate. Luis Marden and photographer Bates Littlehales shared in the dives and prepared articles for publication. Marden described diving into the cenote as a plunge into history. He and other members of the expedition recovered thousands of artifacts, including pottery, masks, a toy clay jaguar, spears, rings, bone awls engraved with hieroglyphs, a clay flute and jade pendants. These and other finds indicated a civilization distinguished by spectacular achievements in architecture, art, astronomy and mathematics.

Submarine archaeology is assuming such importance that many archaeologists are learning the techniques of skin diving. At the University of Florida, Dr. John Goggen pioneered a course for future archaeologists in the use of aqualungs. Already students engaged in underwater research have filled in the blank spots in the history of the Creek Indian Confederacy.

For the submarine archaeologist, safe diving equipment, underwater suction pipes and television cameras have helped in salvaging riches beyond price. Pottery, flutes, spears and watches once drowned but now on exhibit in museums have done much to separate fact from fiction about civilizations of the past.

18

Answers from Archaeology

Whether removed from a tomb in Egypt or a sacred well in Yucatan, the artifacts found by an archaeologist speak to him not of a people long dead, but of a people once alive. What he wants of the knives, axes, baskets and bowls is an understanding of how they were made and used and by whom. To put the human story together, he needs every scrap of information he can get. Like a detective, he sometimes has to reconstruct a drama from scanty, circumstantial evidence.

Archaeologists customarily spend more time in classrooms, laboratories and museums than on expeditions. Some interpretation of their finds is done in the field, but most of it is done after the picks and trowels are put aside.

One of the tedious aspects of the work is assigning dates to the artifacts. Expedition records containing a description of the strata and the relative positions of objects may give the answer. Counting annular rings in a cross section of a building beam unearthed at the dig may provide an estimate of its age. But rings can be deceptive. Possibly the beam has been reused. The archaeologist sometimes establishes a date by associating his finds with known historical happenings. However, many items brought back to the laboratory are prehistoric.

For answers on the really baffling problems of dating, the archaeologist enlists the services of chemists or physicists. One useful laboratory method for dating prehistoric dishes is thermolumines-

179

cence. In this process, pottery is heated to a temperature high enough to release electrons. Although the glow they emit is too faint to be visible, the luminescence can be detected by a photomultiplier tube. The archaeologist knows that the thermal glow is in proportion to the number of years which have elapsed since the object was heated to the same temperature over some ancient campfire. The more light emitted, the greater the age of the pottery.

Many archaeologists find the carbon 14 method of dating useful, but some reject it as inaccurate. This technique, worked out by Nobel Prize winner Dr. Willard Libby and other scientists experimenting with radioactive materials, is based on a number of known facts. Carbon 14, which is constantly being formed in the upper atmosphere by the action of cosmic rays, is present in all living matter. When a plant, person, or animal dies, its carbon 14 content begins to disintegrate.

This disintegration can be measured by what is called "half life." The half life of a pound of carbon 14 will, by radioactivity, be reduced to half a pound in 5,568 years. The half pound will be reduced to a quarter of a pound in another 5,568 years. Because the amount of carbon 14 in the body of anything once alive is measurable, the chemist or archaeologist can determine the length of time disintegration has been going on, or the time of death.

To check the accuracy of the method, Dr. Libby used samples of wood from tombs of Egyptian pharaohs with known dates. Analysis by the carbon 14 method gave the same answers. But errors can creep in. Water percolating through soil in which a bed of charcoal is buried may have leached out some of the radioactive carbon so that parts of a once-living body may not have enough carbon 14 left to be measurable. Moreover, tests on ancient specimens may turn out completely inaccurate, if the amount of radioactive fallout is greatly increased in the atmosphere, as is the case when an atomic bomb is exploded. The other revolutionary measuring tool is the oxygen 18 method developed by another Nobel laureate, Dr. Harold C. Urey.

Chemical tests in a laboratory, which archaeologists on the field lacked equipment or time to carry out, may also reveal answers.

A buckle from a Merovingian cemetery in Belgium came up so rust-encrusted that it appeared worthless, but a penetrating X-ray photograph showed a beautiful design which chemical treatment restored.

Establishing dates and renovating buckles are for the archaeologist only a means to his goal of understanding the where, whys, whats and hows of the past. How did the Lydians in the time of Croesus, or the Americans at the time of Columbus, farm, fight and travel? What did they write, paint, cut or carve? How did an ancient people entertain themselves? Did they have a religion? While searching for his answers to such questions, the laboratory archaeologist is haunted by the fear that important details may have been missed at the dig. Could some small but significant artifact have ended up in the dump pile?

If he is to read the message of the pipes, pots, jewelry and amulets, the archaeologist must be backed by a wealth of scholarly information and he must be able to distinguish between the important and the trivial in reconstructing the cultures of the past from the visible evidence of what its people made, said, did and thought. History tells us much about man since he learned to write, but for the long ninety-nine per cent of time before man mastered this skill we must depend on archaeology.

For many years archaeologists knew more about the people who lived in Pompeii, Troy or Nineveh than they knew about early inhabitants of our own country, but recent expeditions to the Southwest, forays into caves, and a new type of research called pipeline archaeology are filling in the gaps.

Pipeline archaeology originated after scientists and citizens alike realized that many treasure troves would be forever lost unless archaeologists reached them ahead of bulldozers and scoop shovels. Highways, pipelines and flood control projects all threatened destruction of records of the past. The construction of Elephant Butte Dam in the Rio Grande Valley drowned twelve ancient Indian villages, and the same sort of problem came up in other areas.

In 1950 Dr. Jesse L. Nusbaum, consulting archaeologist with the Department of the Interior, heard that the El Paso Natural Gas

Company planned to install two pipelines in northwest New Mexico and in Arizona, one of which would cross the Navajo Indian Reservation. Foreseeing that digging trenches for the pipes could cause irreparable damage to an area rich in artifacts, Nusbaum alerted government officials, Navajo leaders and scientists, and brought pressure on the El Paso Natural Gas Company to finance archaeological investigations before installing the pipes. The company agreed to pay the overall costs of survey and salvage.

Before the bulldozing operations got underway, archaeologists made surface surveys of endangered sites within the staked-out right-of-way. Then they followed in the wake of the trenching machines. Whenever artifacts were exposed, the archaeologists, with help from a digging crew, removed as many objects as possible in the time lag between the ditching and laying down of pipes. All along the New Mexico ditches they found signs of former occupants. Pueblos, pit houses, and ceremonial chambers yielded axes, awls, bowls, pipes and wooden effigies of animals. In Arizona, they found objects similar to those dug up in other sites, plus decorated bones, crude needles, and whistles and flutes made from large bird bones.

The results of the joint effort pleased archaeologists, Navajos, Gas Company and government alike. The pipeline salvage program proved that industry, science, and government can cooperate for the mutual benefit of all. Since then there have been other cooperative ventures combining archaeologists and construction crews. An Inter-Agency Salvage Program backed by over sixty private, university, state and federal agencies has been formed to coordinate pipeline archaeology.

A series of books would be necessary to enumerate the findings on early American culture resulting from pipeline archaeological expeditions. Archaeologists now know that in the Southwest alone eight different cultures followed one another, although—possibly because of the scattered and visible remains of cliff dwellings—interest has centered on the ancient pueblo people who perched on the cliffs for defense and protection.

Seeking answers on the way of life of these primitive people, archaeologists examined everything from hoes to prayer plumes.

A single piece of pottery would raise the questions of the Indians' sources of materials and kinds of kilns, and what, if anything, the decoration on their pottery seemed to suggest or imitate.

Their research pieced together the picture of peaceful, industrious pueblo-dwelling groups of Indians who subsisted largely on beans, squash, corn and pumpkins. Earlier pueblo dwellers raised turkey, but archaeological findings indicate that the Indians were more interested in feathers for prayer plumes than in meat from wild fowl. The round *kivas,* or ceremonial chambers, denoted formal religious rites from early times. That these Indians had artistic ability is demonstrated by remnants of their basketry and pottery.

Archaeologists have unearthed clues to other early cultures in the United States. It seems likely that at Russell Cave near Bridgeport, Alabama, Stone Age men once squatted around flickering fires. Members of an expedition sponsored by the Smithsonian Institution and the National Geographic Society found layer after layer of artifacts there which indicated continuous occupancy from approximately 6,200 B.C. until about 1650 A.D.

What was life like in Russell Cave in 1,000 B.C.? Archaeologists picture a people who killed rabbits or raccoons with stones but hunted bears with spears. They fished with bone hooks and gathered wild grain, nuts and fruits. For jewelry they wore necklaces of bear teeth and bits of shell or bone. They built skin canopies for protection against the water dripping from the roof of their caves. Instead of brushing trash out of the cave, they covered it with soil.

Although archaeologists contribute much to our knowledge of prehistory, they also provide historical insights and are historians in their own right. Famous archaeologist Sir Leonard Woolley once said, "There is no fenced frontier between archaeology and history." The foundations of dwellings and tombs and the scrolls that archaeologists uncover often provide supplementary data. Historians already knew a great deal about Rome and its outlying possessions at the height of the Empire, but a mosaic floor uncovered in Sicily cast new light on the life of noblemen of that period. It depicted an outdoor barbecue, bathing scenes and religious customs. On one mosaic, hunters with spears and shields pursued tigers, leopards and panthers through forests and marshes, over hills and across rivers.

Archaeologists have made many contributions to Biblical history by confirming the location of cities and establishing a factual basis for some Biblical stories. Religious scholars had long asserted that the story of Noah and the flood was a true one, at least so far as the flood itself was concerned, but scoffers disbelieved. Sir Leonard Woolley, after digging a series of trenches in the Tigris-Euphrates Valley, found a great deposit of water-laid clay that attested to a flood, which—although it may not have been of the properties described in the story of Noah—was certainly gigantic.

On the other hand, archaeological discoveries occasionally upset previously recorded religious history. For years textbooks asserted that Saint Augustine brought Christianity to England, but a Christian church excavated near Silchester, supposedly dating back to the fourth century, would seem to indicate that Christianity existed in England before Saint Augustine arrived.

The Dead Sea Scrolls will probably answer more questions about religion than any other find in modern times. On a summer day in 1947 a young Bedouin, Adh-Dhib, lost a goat in an arid, desolate valley near the Dead Sea. Thinking the goat might have strayed into one of the caves in the rocky cliffs along the side of the valley, he began to search them. Perhaps to bolster his courage, perhaps to alert his goat if it lay there, he hurled a rock into one of them. He was startled and ran away when he heard a noise that sounded like pottery shattering, but the next day he returned with a companion.

Inside the cave the goat herders found several jars. One of them contained a large scroll and two smaller ones—all meaningless to the finders, but eventually, after a series of involved transactions, the scrolls came to the attention of scholars and historians. Hopeful that similar scrolls might be hidden in nearby caves, archaeologists hastily organized search parties, which found additional ones. Most of the scrolls were of parchment, but a few were made of papyrus

184

and copper. Some scientists suspected a hoax, but carbon 14 tests proved the discoveries to be authentic. The writings on the scrolls possibly predated the New Testament by a thousand years.

Because the Dead Sea Scrolls are fragmentary and often hard to decipher, it will take years before they can be properly assessed. Some of the material is neither religious nor prophetic, but the part already studied is providing new insights into Judaism and early Christianity. It also provides added details on well-known Bible stories.

Although the Dead Sea Scrolls are being translated and interpreted primarily by scholars and linguists, archaeologists have been able to give valuable advice on handling and preservation.

To answer questions from scholars half a world away from a particular site, archaeologists frequently make copies of inscriptions on the walls of caves or cliffs. Papier mâché squeezes were commonly used by archaeologists in the past, but this method of recording finds fell into disrepute after mice in a British museum ate a printed facsimile of the Behistun Rock, which was the key to deciphering Babylonian cuneiform writing.

A newer method is to clean and wash the inscription and then apply latex. When thoroughly dry, the latex can be loosened and peeled off in complete detail, then rolled up and shipped. Latex squeezes survive rough treatment and are inedible.

More and more often archaeologists are called upon to work out details in the restorations of landmarks or historical sites. In Greece, archaeologists supplied authentic details for the rebuilding of the agora, once the heart of ancient Athens. Colonnades, covered walls, shops and statuary now look much as they did in the day of Pericles and Socrates.

American archaeologists have assisted in many projects designed to re-create the colonial atmosphere of the early days of our country. At Saugus, Massachusetts, there is an ironworks complete in every detail from kettle castings to furnace. The restoration even includes a water wheel, the oldest one in America, which amateur archaeologist Roland Wells Robbins found buried under Central Street in downtown Saugus. Visitors to Jamestown, Virginia, can see the matchlock, musket and siege helmet Captain John Smith used when he commanded the Jamestown guards.

At Williamsburg, Virginia, almost four hundred buildings have been reconstructed on original foundations uncovered by archaeologists. During a period extending over more than thirty years, archaeologists have located sites of colonial taverns, public buildings, private homes, shops, smokehouses and the first theater built in America in 1717.

Out of the excavations came an unending stream of objects and fragments, awls, chisels, brass tacks—even tiny delftware bowls. The estimated 250,000 pieces recovered have become an index of the social, domestic and economic life of the community.

The Williamsburg restoration was accomplished through the teamwork of archaeologists, historians, architects and furnishings specialists. Before any digging was done at the Hay site, for example, historians had traced its history and assembled from many sources biographical data about solid citizen Anthony Hay. A distinguished cabinetmaker, he had, in 1767, purchased the Raleigh Tavern, scene of much of the political agitation preceding the American Revolution.

The biggest reconstruction problem ever tackled by archaeologists was presented by the Aswan Dam construction in Egypt. Being built to harness the Nile River, the dam, when completed, will flood temples and priceless treasures. Archaeologists have been working frantically to remove as many artifacts as possible. A major project is the removal of a temple built in the reign of the Pharoah Rameses II. This operation includes separating the rock-cut edifice from the rest of the cliff, moving it, and reconstructing it on higher ground. Because such an operation almost certainly will cause some damage to the beautiful wall paintings and hieroglyphic inscriptions, archaeologists, artists and photographers are making an exact record of the temple before it is moved.

In Egypt and elsewhere archaeologists often find themselves working and sharing answers with artists. Without the discoveries made through archaeology, the history of art would be both incomplete and erroneous. Although archaeologists are usually less interested than artists in details of line, color and techniques, they contribute to the history and understanding of art through providing facsimiles, revealing the location of cave drawings, and sometimes in actually excavating paintings.

On Rome's Palatine Hill archaeologists recently unearthed a painting which they think may have belonged to Caesar Augustus, grandnephew of Julius Caesar. The modern-looking cylinder in the center of the picture with its needle-nose pointing skyward reminded archaeologists of a Titan or Atlas missile. They dubbed it the "Missile of Augustus."

That piece of art supplied archaeologists with almost no details of the life of its period, but sometimes even such primitive drawings as those found on cave walls in France tell much of the everyday struggle for existence of early man.

The connection between art and archaeology seems more predictable than the tie between archaeology and agriculture, but archaeologists have supplied some answers to agricultural questions too. Scientific-minded farmers of recent times turned to archaeologists when they wondered if inter-breeding kernels of ages-old maize with the species of corn grown today might result in a disease and rust-resistant strain.

While engaged in their studies of maize during the nineteen twenties, archaeologists were fascinated by an ear of petrified corn sent from Peru to the Smithsonian Institution. How could the corn look so much like modern corn? asked archaeologists and botanists who examined it. Finally they decided to use the specimen for investigation rather than for exhibition and sliced it in two. The mystery became immediately apparent. It had been made of potter's clay by some clever Peruvian. The inside was hollow.

Scientists did, however, succeed in locating maize for agricultural studies. Archaeologist Dr. Herbert Dick, working in Bat Cave, New Mexico, discovered a kind of pod corn which carbon 14 tests showed to be 4,300 years old.

Archaeologists played an important role in solving an agricultural riddle which confronted government officials of Iran. In ancient times, officials told the team of archaeologists, geologists and soil scientists, their country had been fertile and productive. Why was it now largely sterile? The team of scientists found that silting had changed the course of river beds and salts had decreased the yield of the soil. Archaeologists pointed out that part of the problem lay in local neglect of the ancient irrigation system, which had clogged up and disappeared from sight. The combined recommendations of the team led to an increased water supply and to better crops for Iranians.

On occasion, archaeologists have been asked to supply answers in boundary disputes. Several times quarrels have arisen among Indian tribes over ownership of land in the Southwest. By digging up pottery and other artifacts of an area and comparing them with those produced by neighboring tribes, archaeologists have been able to determine the probable boundary line.

With such new tools and techniques as Lerici's periscopic tube and pipeline archaeology, archaeologists are making big strides in their interpretation of the stages in the life of man. But the past and the undiscovered resources of archaeology are equally vast. Much that is strange and beautiful has not yet been revealed. In India and in Central America lie known cities that have not been properly excavated. Elsewhere there must certainly be more lost civilizations and lost treasures waiting to be claimed.

Funds are always a problem for archaeological expeditions. So is growing nationalism, for nations which once permitted archaeologists to take artifacts out of their country now impound almost everything of value. But, spurred by the belief that no individual can understand himself or his world without some knowledge of the past, archaeologists pay little attention to obstacles. On deserts and remote islands, in jungles and in caves, they continue to dig up the tools, toys, dishes and weapons that reveal the works, ways and strivings of ancient man. They do it, British archaeologist Geoffrey Bibby once said, "that the past may color the present and give heart to the future."

Postscript

It will not be surprising if the reader of this book comes to the end of it with the feeling of having read an unfinished detective story. The brief glimpses beneath land and sea may give the impression of more questions left unanswered than answered.

The story *is* unfinished. What is important is not that some questions are still unanswered, but that scientists continue to seek the answers. Today, tomorrow, next year, scientific detectives—oceanographers, archaeologists, subsurface geologists, geophysicists and biologists—will uncover hundreds of surprises.

One day the destructive underground and underseas forces, now little more than mysteries, will be met and mastered. The secret places of earth and ocean will yield their treasures for the good of all mankind. Subterranean and submarine scientists do not underestimate the wonders of stars and space, but they do not neglect the wonders beneath the land and the sea.

Index

OF SUBJECTS AND UNFAMILIAR TERMS

191